Miss Emily

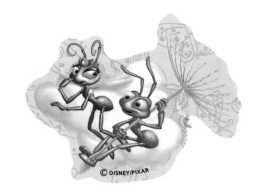

Miss Emily

Emily Howland, teacher of freed slaves, suffragist and friend of Susan B. Anthony and Harriet Tubman. With excerpts from her diaries and letters

Mildred D. Myers

Tabby House

Manufactured in the United States of America

Library of Congress Catalog Card Number: 98-60582

ISBN: 1-881539-20-2

Cover design: Pearl and Associates

Chapter illustration: "The Allée," Joy Duperault

Tabby House

4429 Shady Lane
Charlotte Harbor, FL 33980
(941) 629-7646

With gratitude and love

This book is dedicated to Phebe King (1894–1982):
Student, teacher and principal in Miss Emily's school in
Sherwood in the 'teens and 1920s.
Boarder in Miss Emily's home, and her close friend and admirer.
Author of eight booklets about Miss Emily and her school.
Custodian of Miss Emily's original materials
and sponsor of and inspiration for this book.

Acknowledgments and Notes

This book has truly been a community project. It could never have been written without the memories, historical knowledge, corrections and editing help, loans of materials, and the encouragement of literally dozens of people.

You know who you are. Please also know that I am endlessly and enormously grateful to each and every one of you.

And some explanatory notes:

Miss Emily's use of "thee," "thy" and "thine" throughout this book reflects the old-time Quaker usage in speaking to one another. "Thee" was singular, so when they spoke to more than one person they said "you."

Also, Miss Emily referred to her early efforts as working for Woman Suffrage. Later she spoke of Woman's Suffrage.

In our century, this has become the Women's Rights movement.

Friends Meeting referred to the gathering of Quakers (more properly known as Friends) for worship and business.

The chapter headings are taken from a nineteenth century book, *Language of Flowers*.

Carpetbaggers were Northern opportunists who went South after the Civil War and took advantage of the political and domestic turmoil. They often carried their belongings in suitcases made out of carpet-like materials.

Contents

On Writing Emily's Story

In 1947 when I came to Sherwood to teach in the school that Emily Howland built, she was still vividly remembered by neighbors and alumni as one who had changed their lives for the better.

A dear older friend of mine, Phebe King, first had been a student in Emily's Sherwood Select School, then she came back from Cornell to teach there and became the principal for its last two years under Emily's sponsorship. Phebe loved and valued Emily, and wanted a book written to keep her memory alive. I promised to write it.

But from the very first, this book took one step back for every two steps forward, due to the never-ending influx of fresh information, starting with several boxes from Phebe, from repositories (Swarthmore, Cornell, Wells College), from news clippings and letters and from interviews with those who remembered her. Clearly Emily spent much of her one hundred years with her pen in hand! And all this mountain of data added to or corrected what I'd already written.

Luckily, before Phebe sent Emily's diaries to the Swarthmore College archives, the excerpts, which helped shape the book, had been made. The excerpts revealed what the Sherwood community had not known—that Emily had enjoyed a special longtime friendship with Col. Charles Folsom that started during the Civil War.

After that promising beginning, they wrote back and forth for forty years and the colonel's letters were among Emily's papers, which her niece, Isabel Howland, received and later entrusted to Phebe King. Unfortunately, Phebe loaned them, they left the area and have not yet returned. So without his letters, the story of Emily and Colonel Folsom is based on Emily's diary references about him.

Through all this research and rewriting, Miss Emily has become very real and dear to me. Now, as this twenty-year project draws to a close, I hope to place the research materials entrusted to me in the Wells College archives in nearby Aurora, for the use of all.

MILDRED D. MYERS

The Howland Stone Store at Sherwood. Built by Slocum Howland in 1837, it operated as a country store until 1884. The cobblestone restoration work shown in progress was begun in 1996. The building at left is "The Block." Built in 1884 by William Howland, it operated as a country store from then until 1975.

Foreword

Today we often forget the long struggle that Emily Howland and many like-minded people, mainly women, endured to bring about women's suffrage and other rights. Though Mrs. Myers has chosen to write as a novel, all of her characters are "real." After her many years of reading and research, she has woven an accurate and meaningful story of "Miss Emily," her family, her friends and her times. She has acutely identified Miss Emily's "causes" and her means of promoting them. Readers will easily identify with her sensitivities, doubts, loyalties and feelings of responsibility.

The Howlands came to Central New York in the late 1790s seeking good lands and agricultural opportunities, as well as freedom as Quakers to pursue their pacific, antislavery and educational views. Their prosperity then encouraged their philanthropic goals, and gave opportunity for their sons and daughters to excel in their efforts. Miss Emily was one of the remarkable women this sect either gave rise to, such as Susan and Lucy Anthony, Lucretia Mott, and Matilda Gage, or enabled to reach their goals, including such local women as Dr. Amanda Sanford Hickey, Dr. Eliza Mosher, Agnes Tierney, Dr. Susan Otis, Ann Searing, Jane (Jennie) Slocum, and Dr. Katie Munhall.

BRADLEY MITCHELL
President and Curator
Howland Stone Store Museum
Sherwood, New York

Prologue

1927

Emily, leaning to her mirror and trying to pin her floral brooch at the neck of her black gown with her stiff old fingers, turned as the door opened. "Good, thee is just in time, Isabel." She held out the brooch to her niece and tipped up her chin.

Belle, having fastened the pin, looked her over carefully and patted her arm approvingly. "Happy birthday, dear Aunt," she said, with a warm kiss. "Imagine you, my very own Aunt Emily, one hundred years old!"

Emily smoothed the black silk skirt of her gown, and asked, "Is anyone coming yet?"

"No, it's still a little early."

"Then let's sit down a moment. I'm in no hurry to go down and be lionized."

Belle chuckled indulgently. "Oh, Aunt Emily, you remember last year how you tried to get out of going to Albany for your honorary degree. It's just your terrible modesty. But you know you'll enjoy every minute of it."

Her aunt said seriously, "I can't make it fit me at all, to be honored now for being out of step all my life!"

"Why do you say you were out of step, Aunt?"

"If it wasn't my mother making me come home from boarding school because she said nobody would marry an overeducated female, then she was throwing up her hands at my wanting to go to that first woman's rights meeting in Seneca Falls!" Wonderingly, she added, "I always had to fight for anything I most dearly wanted to do. There was always *someone* to say I *must* not!"

"I don't remember Grandmother much. She was never well and she was not a cozy grandmother, was she?"

"No," Emily agreed. "But it wasn't just Mother. The neighbors thought it a great joke when I carried petitions for woman suffrage. And they certainly thought it was queer for me to go off alone to Washington to teach school for young colored women."

"It may have been unusual, but that's one of the main reasons people want to honor you today!" Looking at her lovingly, Isabel added, "I can't get over your turning a hundred years old! Where did the years go?" She shook her head, and then asked, hesitantly, "Looking back, are you sorry you never married?"

Emily looked over her spectacles inquiringly.

"I never met the colonel, but I always knew of him from Mother," explained Isabel, "and also, you'll remember that I went to Manassas with you when you dedicated the water plant as a memorial to him."

Emily paused. "Well, neither he nor I could compromise on the rights of women. I was determined to work for the ballot, and he was just as determined that no wife of his would do any such thing!"

Isabel took her hand. "Well, you and I got to work with the great ones in that long struggle, didn't we? Dear Aunt Susan and the others."

Emily smiled reminiscently.

"And it was surely a great moment when you spoke before Congress in 1904, wasn't it?"

Emily shook her head. "I never counted that as a triumph. We met with precious little enthusiasm there, and it took sixteen more years for you younger women to finally win us the vote!"

She cocked her head. "Is that an automobile I hear?"

Isabel rose and drew back the curtain. "Yes, in fact there are three, no, four coming. We'd better go down now, Aunt Emily." Helping her up, Isabel added, "This won't be any ordeal. These will all be people you know well, who love and admire you."

Emily demurred, "But all this fuss just doesn't seem right for plain Emily Howland!"

Mountain Pink: "Aspiration"

1856

Emily hurried up Senator Seward's front walk, hoping, no, *craving* to see her friend. Over and over she had pondered her unsettled future this morning, while lurching to Auburn with Father in the market wagon, through twelve miles of deep spring ruts. After cutting her errands to barest necessities in order to save this precious time, she had hastened back out South Street for a heartening visit with Mrs. Seward until Father should stop by for her on his way home.

Mrs. Seward's smiling welcome and the promise of tea warmed and cheered her. They had barely settled themselves, however, when the maid again summoned Mrs. Seward to the door, and Emily heard a man's voice in the hall. Why, it was Father saying, "He needs the money right away, so I can get this load of whale oil cheap if I can catch the train now."

Emily started up as they appeared in the doorway, Father, of course, wearing his broad Quaker hat. She noted with approval that he had wiped his boots thoroughly, for Auburn, though a bustling young county seat, still was called by travelers "the worst mud hole in New York State."

"I looked in at the livery stable but there aren't any of the neighbors' rigs there from Sherwood's Corners, and it is the wrong day for the stagecoach." Father chewed his lip as he looked at Emily in perplexity. "Now what am I going to do?"

Her heart sank, but Mrs. Seward immediately said in the most gracious way, "You must leave Emily here with me, Mr. Howland." She added, smiling, "Fanny and I shall be more than happy."

Father, lingering only to ask, "Has thee enough money for the stagecoach in the morning?" and to nod his thanks, was gone.

Emily felt awkward until Mrs. Seward said warmly, "How pleasant this will be! When we go upstairs, I shall find you a night robe and toilet articles. We are always ready for company in this house, but rarely do I enjoy them as much as I shall enjoy having you here."

Reassured by her hostess's affectionate manner, Emily's spirits soared. Chuckling, she said, "Well, if thee must give me my dinner, I beg thee will not think of inviting any eligible bachelors."

Mrs. Seward, though married before Emily was born, nevertheless was a dear friend who always entered into Emily's feelings, listening with her whole heart. Emily had often called on her while Father consulted with Senator Seward, and sometimes played with the children, but never had she had Mrs. Seward all to herself like this, with the rest of the afternoon and the evening before them.

As Mrs. Seward poured their tea, she inquired, smiling, "Now, what is all this about eligible suitors?"

"Oh, Mother and a couple of the old aunts from Meeting are always saying if I don't hurry and get myself a husband, the other girls will have them all."

Mrs. Seward's eyes twinkled at Emily's scorn, but her smile was very kind.

"A worthy young man did ask for my hand awhile back and I could not bring myself to accept him. They will never let me forget it."

Frances Seward's indulgent smile faded and she leaned forward anxiously, laying a hand fleetingly on Emily's sleeve. "But are you sure you will never regret it yourself? The security of marriage, that is? A single woman can be so very alone."

"I doubt that I shall ever want to marry." Regarding her friend fondly, Emily added, "It is different for thee, of course. But no, my dream is quite otherwise. When they made me come home from Mary Grew's School in Philadelphia," and here she took a deep breath, "I was planning to take medical training."

"Medical training!" Mrs. Seward's teacup hung in midair as she gazed at Emily in amazement. "Could you have done so?"

"Friend Lucretia Mott had just at that time promised to ask a female physician who had trained in Europe to take me as an apprentice."

Mrs. Seward's deep attention encouraged Emily to go on, "They've let me go back awhile each winter since, assuming I was visiting my school friends, but in truth I've been attending evening classes at the new Female Medical College, preparing in a small way in case there might sometime be a chance." Her voice dropped. "But there never will be." She shook her head hopelessly. "I do not believe Father would pay for my training, and if he would, Mother would never let me go."

After a pause while Mrs. Seward's eyes searched Emily's face, she said, "You are much braver than I am, Emily, to aspire to such a radical career. I do not even dare give funds to Elizabeth Cady Stanton's work for woman's rights, for I simply could not live with Mr. Seward's ridicule."

"Father has been willing to back my bits of work for Mrs. Stanton, but even that has been a great disappointment." Here Emily remembered how confidently she had written to Elizabeth Cady Stanton two years ago:

Albany, Mar. 15, 1854
My dear Mrs. Stanton:

I came here yesterday. The woman's property bill passed the House and we are promised final action in the Senate tomorrow when, I hope, we shall get the Governor's signature and it will become the law of the State of New York.

Yours in haste,

Emily Howland

Now, to this sympathetic listener, she admitted, "I was so green when I first went to Albany, I was dumfounded when they turned our woman's property bill over to a committee that disposed of it by declaring that God Himself had mandated that man and woman shall never be equal." Both of them frowned and shook their heads over this.

Emily clasped her hands together tightly and studied them a moment before saying, "In any case, I would so much prefer to practice medicine among the needful ones of the colored race." Then looking up, she said desperately, "If I can't do that, what am I going to do with myself?"

Mrs. Seward, looking at her young friend's discouraged face, hesitated and then impetuously declared, "I have a strong conviction about you, Emily. Ever since I first saw your knack with my children, when you played with them in the nursery, I have felt you were born to teach."

The last three words hung in the air. There was a long pause while the younger woman gazed wonderingly at her, then into the distance. Her lips moved, soundlessly, forming the words "born to teach."

Mrs. Seward waited patiently until she came back to the present. Then, her hopeful look fading, Emily said drearily, "Oh well, I do not suppose I would be allowed to do that either."

Mrs. Seward set her cup aside and leaned forward to pat Emily's hand. "Well, I am very glad to have you here." Then rising, she added, "Now, I know Fanny wants you to herself, and then we both will need a little rest before dinner."

Emily's preparations for dinner were limited to brushing out her long, thick, dark hair, twisting it back up smoothly, and washing her face and hands. She did not admire what she saw in the mirror, overlooking her eager-eyed face and noting only that she was unsuitably garbed to dine with a senator. A maid had brushed the mud from the hem of her long dark gown, but it was neither fresh nor fashionable. At least it was of good heavy silk, because the Quakers used no cotton fabrics which required slave labor, and it was not made as plainly as the old-time Quaker costume which Mother wore.

Emily consoled herself, as well, that Mrs. Seward never dressed to cast anyone in the shade. In fact, when a much-younger Emily had complained that she wished she could wear bright colors and flowers in her bonnet, Mrs. Seward had smiled, but said mildly that for herself, she felt more comfortable being inconspicuous.

William Henry Seward, formerly governor of New York and now a United States senator, seemed glad to find Emily at his dinner table, perhaps because her visits gave pleasure to his retiring wife and twelve-year-old daughter, Fanny. Or perhaps it was because she was well informed on the issues of the day, even if she sometimes suspected from the glint in his eyes that he found her opinions naïve.

When their dessert of jelly roll was placed before them, he asked for apples to be brought also, explaining, "The Orson pippins were especially fine this winter." Then he said to Emily, "I've never thought to ask your father what became of that slave who came to Sherwood's Corners in the forties with his baby in a bag on his back."

"Oh, yes," she nodded, "that was Hermon Phillips with little Harriet, and his wife and three other young ones. He told us, 'Old Master was going to sell my boys down South.' And no one who had seen his beaming smile as he pushed those two handsome little fellows forward could ever again claim, 'Colored folks don't love their children or feel pain at parting with them like white people do.'"

"I should think not," exclaimed Mrs. Seward, startled.

"Well, Father settled them in a snug little house on the Stage Road, and Hermon went right to work, helping him in all kinds of ways around the store. But in 1850, when he heard of that infamous law that allowed slaves to be pursued and recaptured anywhere in the Union, Hermon cried out that his master would catch his boys and sell them down into Georgia. He took his family and fled to Canada where they almost perished with the cold, until Father collected enough to pay Hermon's ransom. Then he brought him back as a free man, and resettled them all in their little house. The boys are big enough now to be nearly as good help as their father."

Mrs. Seward had listened, enthralled. "How grateful Mr. Phillips must be," she exclaimed.

"Oh, yes, Hermon always says of Father, 'Now ain't that man a saint!'"

The senator smiled at this, but nodded too, for he respected and valued Slocum Howland, Emily knew.

She continued thoughtfully, "I've wondered how they ever found their way. All Hermon will say is they followed the North Star. But how could they know the safe places and avoid the perils?" Turning to Seward, she asked, "Can thee tell me how the Underground Railroad works?"

The senator's eyes dropped to the apple he was peeling. "Those particulars would be hard to come by. The runaways have always risked beatings and possible death, and now anyone harboring them may be arrested for treason, and risks violent reprisals as well. It is understandable that there are no details to be heard."

Thoughtfully, Emily remarked, "We children were taught to sympathize with the slaves, reading the *Anti-Slavery Record*, and hearing two or three of the great Abolitionist speakers at Meeting each year. And Harriet Beecher Stowe's heart-stirring book, *Uncle Tom's Cabin* told how brave Quaker folk gave aid to the fugitives. I'm greatly disappointed that Father is not in the forefront of this heroic work."

At this, the senator's hands paused in their task for an instant and his eyes flicked up, but failed to meet hers. Then he launched smoothly into an account of two runaway slaves who had recently been hidden in a raft-load of barn lumber to be towed by ferry from Seneca County across Cayuga Lake. He finished, "Just as the ferry pushed off, the pursuing agents rushed up, jumped aboard and, all unsuspecting, rode across to King's Ferry along with the very slaves they were hunting."

Though the senator had told the story amusingly, he somehow lacked his usual ease of manner. Watching him intently, Emily thought it was almost as if he were trying to distract her. At the end, without any pause, he put down his uneaten apple and fruit knife, and wiped his fingers while saying to his wife, "Well, my dear, my compliments on the dinner."

Emily, putting down her napkin and rising, felt rebuffed by the oddity of it all: the tiny flicker of his eyes, and his manner so flowingly sociable that she could not interpose a word. Suddenly she saw it all. *Why, Father is part of the Underground Railroad, and the senator knows all about it!*

She felt her face flushing with quick, hot resentment against these so-superior men for shutting her out. As she thought it over later, in Mrs. Seward's comfortable guest room, she realized that no secret would be safe if all the women in Sherwood's Corners knew it. Even the senator had given it away to her, in one unguarded moment. But what a fool he must think she was!

Years later she was to realize that it had never occurred to her to look to *Mrs.* Seward for information.

Now however, she suddenly chuckled to herself. She, Emily Howland, had managed to ruffle Senator Seward's "marvelous imperturbability" with which, so the press reported, he superbly ignored all insults from his fellow senators about his antislavery stand. She was still smiling at this absurdity as she snuggled down in bed.

Then her thoughts turned irresistibly back to Mrs. Seward's saying she was born to teach. To get an education had been a burning object, even a necessity, to her. Would it not be fine to help other young women to achieve their schooling? There were several select schools in Auburn now, and she would need only a little preparation. Yes, it might be possible. A position as teacher might open to her, someday.

Throwing the covers aside restlessly, she went to the window and kneeling, her arms folded on the sill, she leaned out. The moonlight changed the familiar street scene, silvering the trees against the dark. It was like seeing the world backward, she thought. And as she looked, suddenly she was also seeing her life in a new light. To practice medicine was never going to be possible. The old dream must go.

Instead, perhaps she *was* born to teach.

This idea rooted itself strongly in Emily's mind and when she was home again, she tentatively suggested teaching. Mother of course ignored her and turned the conversation, but Emily was not about to give up so easily.

She could not be satisfied to live as a Quaker woman in this little hamlet. Though close to the busy stagecoach inn and Father's general store at the crossroads, she was expected to keep herself separate from all that bustle, making her existence in housework, sewing for escaped slaves, and attending Meeting.

In the newspaper, she read Seward's remark: "The colored people, even when delivered out of slavery, will never live more nobly until they are *elevated by education*."

As she reread his words, in a flash of insight her two separate goals, to teach and to help the colored people, met and merged. Her Grandfather Tallcot, who had tutored her as a child, had repeatedly quoted Bacon's words, "Learning is power." Well, if she were to teach colored people, she could put that power in their hands. But how was she ever to reach these people?

In the meantime, Emily had not forgotten Senator Seward's strange manner at dinner which had convinced her that under her very nose, the Friends were somehow passing runaway slaves through Sherwood's Corners. Now she was watching sharply for any telltale signs.

At breakfast one morning, Father's usual piece of pie was missing from his place. She got up quietly and went to the pantry, then stepped into the kitchen. "Becky, I thought there was quite a chunk of that mince pie left from supper."

The cook's face took on an expression that Emily could not read and then she said uncomfortably, "Well...I guess not."

Emily looked searchingly at her. She would have declared that Becky was the most honest woman she knew. Back at the table, she said as she sat down, "There seems to be no pie this morning." Then glancing at Father, she saw an expression so fixed as to be almost glassy.

Of course! It all fitted in. Father was taking a hand in passing along fugitive slaves, and Becky was drawn into it to furnish their food. But Sherwood's Corners was a main stagecoach stop between Auburn and Ithaca, and exceedingly public. How were these refugees being spirited from one place to another? This began to worry her. If a rescue should ever depend on her alone, what would she do? At last a plan grew in her mind.

Her chance came one evening when she was alone downstairs. Father had gone to the funeral of an elderly relative in Skaneateles and would not be home until very late, and perhaps not at all, for it was at the dark of the moon. Mother had assumed he would stay over and ride home in daylight, so she had gone up to bed. Becky, being day help, had gone home. Just as Emily happened into the kitchen for fresh candles, she heard a stick of firewood roll down the woodpile. A stable cat must have slipped into the back woodshed, she supposed. But when she opened the further door and lifted her lamp to peer around, the light fell upon a large black man cowering against the stacked wood and staring in terror.

The thought flashed through her mind that fugitives must be told to let themselves into this woodshed upon their arrival in Sherwood's Corners, to await help. But tonight there was no one here to help him but herself.

"Oh please, missy, I won't hurt you!" the man gasped.

Emily, far from frightened, eagerly ordered, "Wait here. I'll be back with clothes and food." She snatched up a part loaf in the kitchen and ran back to thrust it into his hands. Then again leaving him in darkness, she ran upstairs for the voluminous gray cloak, Quaker bonnet and shawl she had earlier laid ready in her chest.

Downstairs again, she threw on her own wraps and hurried to the shed where she handed the garments to the man. His hands were shaking so much he could not tie the bonnet on, and she impatiently tied the bow under his chin. Then, blowing out her candle, she whispered, "Come."

They tiptoed out the back door and toward the stable, but she stopped so suddenly at a noise that he almost bumped into her. The two of them froze, listening intently. Was someone in the stable? Or was someone outside lurking about, waiting and watching?

She looked up at the fugitive. She could see only the whites of his wide eyes, inside the bonnet, as they searched the darkness from side to side.

Suddenly her heart pounded in her ears. If this adventure went awry, what would it cost this terrified man who had risked such dangers to get this far? What tortures would he be dragged back to? And Father... exposure would destroy him as a "stationmaster." And marshals could impose heavy fines and likely imprisonment... on whom? Herself? No, they would doubtless hold Father responsible.

The stable door began to creak open, slowly, slowly, and then a dark figure slipped out and came silently toward them. It was almost upon them when a hand shot out and clutched her arm, and her older brother, William, hissed angrily, "What is thee doing here?"

With a great gasp of relief, she whispered, "Oh, William! I was going to drive him to...."

"Yes, miss, to where?" He shook her arm.

"To Sewards', as a Quaker nurse, saying they needed nursing help for a child."

Even in the dark she could feel him staring at her. "Thee would lead them straight to Seward?"

To the black man he whispered, "Get those things off," and then, fiercely, to her, as he bundled them into her arms, "Get that stuff out of sight as fast as thee can and speak no word to anyone!" Then they were gone.

Emily stumbled back up the stairs and quickly laid the clothes away. She stood in the middle of the floor, clasping her hands against her heaving chest until she could quiet her breathing. Then, after blowing out her lamp, she tiptoed to the empty back bedroom and peered out of the window. The stable yard below was dark and quiet. Leaning against the window casing, she knew one of her bitterest moments. Oh, why had she never thought of William being in the secret? Now she had made a fool of herself a second time. Why couldn't they trust her?

Despite her restless night, she woke early to the familiar sounds of the loading of barrels of pork in brine from her father's packing house next door. This load would be hauled to the wharf at Levanna and shipped up Cayuga Lake to the canal and on to New York City.

She threw her double-gown around her shoulders and again tiptoed through the hall to the back window. The glass panes were so bubbly, she knelt on the bare boards and noiselessly raised the window sash, to watch. Father and William slid the last barrels onto the wagon and William fetched the horses out and hitched them three abreast. By this time her ankles were aching with cold and closing the window, she rose. As William drove the ponderous rig out of the yard, however, she suddenly realized the hour must be very early indeed. Father must have had practically no sleep at all! It was hardly first light, and none of the help was about yet.

Ah! She smiled. The pork barrels! So the fugitive was being spirited safely away. Then her smile faded. Father and William would save fugitives while she filled lamps and dusted the parlor. There was nothing she did that any serving maid could not do as well.

William was considerably later than usual when he drove the empty wagon back into the yard that afternoon. Emily, watching anxiously, saw that as he threw the reins to the stable boy he appeared as calm as usual.

It was not until Emily and her parents were sitting in the parlor after supper that William came in to report to Slocum Howland. "The boat was in early today, but still I was in ample time." He sat down and stretched out his legs wearily. "I must tell thee of a strange happening, Father. Thee knows I was to go on from Levanna to deliver those plow points in Union Springs, and then take a barrel of pork to the Seward home in Auburn. I did so, setting it off in the side yard. Then I went on to the blacksmith to have one of the black mare's shoes tended to. When I drove back out South Street, I noticed the top had been knocked off the barrel at Seward's."

Emily stopped breathing for a moment.

William continued, "I stopped and hammered the lid back on. The pork was not dumped nor disturbed. Now was that not curious, Father?"

William held Emily's eyes with a long, steady look before her father replied, slowly, "That was indeed curious, William." Emily saw the look that passed between the two men as Slocum Howland nodded in satisfaction.

It was all right then. Clearly William had led the pursuer off on a false scent and the fugitive was safe. Perhaps he was now one station closer to the freedom awaiting him on the Canadian side of the border.

In her room, Emily reviewed all this. Was he really on a canal boat? Or was he still hidden in Father's warehouse in Levanna, waiting for some small boat? Or was he right next door here in the packing house, among the close-hanging hog carcasses and clusters of hogshead barrels, to be moved in some other ingenious way?

Emily soon found that, though she knew nothing, it was sometimes an advantage. An older neighbor woman came bringing them some of her pears, an unusual gesture from her. Even more unusual were the questions she proceeded to ask. "Emily, how old were you when your father's store was a-building?"

"Why, I scarcely know. Let me see. I suppose I was nine or ten."

"Did you watch the building of it?" persisted the woman with a curious sideways look.

"Not very often," said Emily with a sigh, remembering the many times she had begged to go watch with her little brother, Ben, and had been set at some chore instead.

When the neighbor remarked carelessly, "I suppose there's a cellar under it," an alarm sounded in Emily's brain. No one knew, these days, who was merely curious and who might be an informer, hoping for bounty money.

"I'm afraid I was very young and heedless," Emily said evasively, and quickly thanked the woman again for the pears.

This conversation set Emily to wondering. She had occasionally been in Father's storage cellar under his general store. Could there be a small hidden space, behind all the wooden boxes? Doubtless it was safer that she should not know too much, for she could not possibly dissemble if questioned more closely.

However, to William's wife Hannah, who was also her closest friend, she did complain, "'Tis hard to be shut out from any part in the stirring deeds of these times, and set at housework."

Hannah and Emily had declared themselves to be sisters when they were childhood playmates, and Mother had never fussed when they were together, declaring Emily would get in no trouble because Hannah "was so steady." These childhood "sisters" had become doubly so when Hannah married William. Emily would never have chosen such a serious and almost dour creature as William for her dear Hannah, yet the two had been devoted to each other for years before they were married. And perhaps, Emily admitted to herself, it was because William, four years her senior, had always felt responsible for her that he was so severe. He certainly was a different man with Hannah. But she wished he had more of her younger brother's sweetness.

Ben, four years younger than herself, had always been accepting of her doings and as a little fellow had usually wanted to do them with her.

She still vividly remembered lingering wistfully by the pump in the backyard, where little Ben was squishing his toes in the mud, and twelve-year-old William, pumping Mother's buckets full, was warning sharply, "Thee must not get thy shoes wet." And Mother, in the doorway, was putting her hand to her forehead and crying out, "Emily Howland, look at the hem of that skirt! And thy petticoats will be as bad. Keeping up with thy washing is dreadful."

"But Mother, it's so hot! Why do I have to wear petticoats and stockings when the boys are barefoot?"

"Because young ladies must. And by the time thee is almost eight, I should think thee would know it."

Ben, upset over her scolding, had followed Emily to the front steps where she was sitting dejectedly. Leaning against her and slipping his small, dirty hand into hers, he had whispered, "Never mind, Emmy."

Even now, they were the best of companions, and if Ben, who was working for Father in the Auburn woolen manufactory, were here to take part in these daring deliverances, *he* would not shut her out so coldly.

To Hannah she now said vigorously, "I have energy and a brain as good as William's, and I wish to serve!"

Hannah nodded. "I know." She hesitated as though she would like to say more, but Father brought in the mail just then, saying, "I must get back to the store now."

Glancing through the pile, Emily picked out a letter. "Hannah, if thee will forgive me, this is from a Philadelphia friend and I must just see if she has any special news."

She quickly scanned the first page. "Yes, she says Miss Myrtilla Miner still needs a teacher for her Normal School for Colored Girls in Washington." Fervently, she added, "How much I wish I could go!"

At that moment, strong as her desire was, she certainly had no expectation of going to Washington, and Hannah could only shake her head sadly.

In talking later with Frances Seward, Emily mourned, "Anything I've ever most dearly wished to do was precisely what I must not do. Thee remembers how Mother had Father fetch me home from school in Philadelphia, saying it was a mistake for girls to get too much education. If I hadn't been able to study my French by myself, and work on my wildflower collection, I don't know what would have become of me then. And that momentous woman's rights convention in Seneca Falls was only twenty miles from home, so close I could almost have walked, and they would not permit me to go! And now here is this position, so exactly what I have wished to do, to teach and by so doing to help colored people to rise, and when will such a chance come again?"

Mrs. Seward looked thoughtful. "Sometimes opportunities open because you have prepared yourself. I have a friend, Phebe Coffin, who has a select school here in Auburn. I know she once gave lessons in teaching to a young woman and then allowed her to instruct a class. 'Practice teaching,' Miss Coffin called it. Would you care to let me speak to her about that possibility? A mere inquiry would commit you to nothing more."

The query led to an invitation to Emily to prepare a single lesson and take one class, to see if she would wish to continue.

Emily knew it would never do to tell Mother about this plan. However, she did occasionally make a visit to a friend. If she wished to stay with a Miss Coffin, an acquaintance of Mrs. Seward's, Mother made no objection, and William could drop her when he next went to Auburn.

Nothing could have been easier, and her success with her first class led to several weeks of instruction and practice teaching. At last she felt fairly competent, and Phebe Coffin commended her aptitude and industry.

It was an anticlimax to return home, all prepared to teach and to have to resume the round of household chores Mother assigned her. She did, of course, tell Hannah all about her pleasure in teaching.

Unexpectedly Hannah responded, "It would be Mother Howland who would most oppose thy wish to teach, would it not?"

"Yes, Father might not like it, but only that once did he truly interfere." Emily frowned at the memory of being torn from her schooling in Philadelphia. "Well, I do try to remember that Mother is not well."

"Why should thee say Mother Howland is not well?"

Emily blinked at her. "Surely thee has seen Mother put her hand to her forehead?"

Hannah nodded. "Often and often I have seen this, and each time, thee was saying something she did not wish to hear, or doing something she did not want thee to do."

Emily stared. Then in her mind's eye, she looked back down the years. Yes, there were the times she had wanted to go out and play with Ben, or to study her French instead of making preserves, or to go to a political meeting with Father, or she was asking to go back to school. All those times when Emily was being awkward, Mother had pressed her hands to her temples!

"It is undutiful of me to have said this," added Hannah, "but the years are flying by and she keeps thee by her side. Emily dear, I want to see thee have thine own life."

Emily looked out the window and to her eyes, all was radiance. "Thee thinks I might break away?"

"I have heard thee wishing to teach at that normal school for colored girls. I can see no reason why thee should not. I would undertake to tend to Mother Howland in thine absence."

Emily was not usually demonstrative, but at this she wordlessly threw her arms around her friend. Dear Hannah, who would add a second household to her cares, to give Emily freedom to go! Now she would actually be able to accept Miss Miner's position, if she could get her parents' backing.

As she came in the back door, her mother called from the cellar, "Emily, is that thee? Please fetch down that last pan of pickles on the table."

When Emily had dumped the pickles into the waiting crock and covered it, she straightened herself to find her mother complacently surveying the crowded shelves and the crocks and barrels around the walls. "Does it not give thee satisfaction to see our storeroom filled for winter from our labor?"

"No, Mother," replied Emily quietly, "I cannot say it does. The satisfaction I crave is in working with people. And Mother," she exclaimed in rising excitement, "school teachers are needed for Negro females in the South. Teaching is something I know I could...do...."

Her voice dwindled as her mother put her hand to her head and dragged herself up the stairs. "Will thee please to fetch that pan back up when thee comes," floated back to Emily in a thin thread of voice.

Emily sat down on the edge of the potato bin, overcome with the old feeling of guilt. But no, why should she feel so? Jumping up, she determined to go in search of Father who had invited her to ride along with him this afternoon to inspect a farm on which he might take a mortgage. This was her chance to tell him about the Miner School. It might be futile, but she was not going to give up her dream for want of trying.

On the other hand, she must not cast the seed too hastily, without first preparing the ground. So as they rode along, she said, "Father, thy friend Senator Seward says the slaves, even when freed, can never live nobly until they are elevated by education."

Father considered this and nodded. "That sounds like William Seward. I am in complete agreement with him."

She let him think this over awhile as they jogged along, and then told him about the need for a teacher at the Miner Normal School for Colored Girls.

Father understood her immediately. With a searching look, he enquired, "Is thee qualified?"

This was the hardest part. "I must admit I let thee and Mother believe I was merely visiting Phebe Coffin when in truth I was teaching in her school to gain experience."

Father looked very grave. "Was that deception necessary, Emily?"

"I felt it was, Father. It was what I needed to do, according to my Inner Light, and I knew it was the only way I could do it."

They jogged on. Father sat silent and to her apprehensive eyes, his profile looked forbidding. Emily's heart sank.

After a long pause, he said calmly, "If thee wants to teach in Virginia, I would support thee in that enterprise," and here he paused while her spirits soared. Then he added, "...if thee can convince thy mother."

Emily's heart sank again. How could she face Mother's sighs and accusing looks? In the end, she wrote from Auburn:

July 29 1857
Dear Mother:

> *Now I am going to write upon the matter in my thoughts because it is easier to write than to talk of it. It is, may I work a little while for that class which has so long enlisted my closest sympathies? May I try if I really can make the world a little better for having lived in it? If all my life is to go on as have the last years, I know I shall feel at the end of it as tho' I had lived in vain. Now the opportunity is mine, such a one may not come again. Let me improve it!*

> > *Farewell affectionately,*

> > *Emily*

And to her Philadelphia correspondent she also wrote from Auburn:

> *Though I cannot teach at all to my satisfaction, yet I find pleasure & satisfaction & cheerfulness that I have not known for years. I had a letter from Miss Miner; she seemed very discouraged by recent threats against the school. She said she could not advise me in the matter of going, I must act according to my own convictions. If it is right to go, would it not be wrong to waver in view of possible danger?*

Though Emily still had to face Mother, she would certainly tell her nothing of any possible dangers. And with Hannah's promise to help about the house, and Father's promise to finance Emily's trip, all the poor woman could do was to look disapproving. She did say, "I expect thee will find it all beyond thee and be glad enough to come along home where thee belongs." She followed this with many heavy sighs and a series of severe headaches.

Emily also had to endure the vehement disapproval of some of the older women in the Friends' Meeting.

All this unpleasantness was lightened by Mrs. Seward's insistence that Emily must come to them in Washington as often as she could, when the Senate was in session.

She was also cheered by a note from Ben, ever her friend and comfort, bless him:

Well I am sincerely glad that thee had finally decided to
do what thee ought (for thy own happiness) to have done
long ago. As for what the world may say, I wouldn't care
a straw.

Some of her elation had been rubbed off by all this struggle, which led her to feel, during her two-day trip to Washington by carriage, steamer and train, that nothing she might face there could be much worse.

Wild Plum: "Independence"

1857

Emily was not so confident when at last she stood before her class, as the unpaid assistant in Miss Miner's pioneering Normal School for Colored Girls on the outskirts of Georgetown.

The resistance she felt from these young women around the long tables was very different from the gentleness of Miss Coffin's Quaker school. She sympathized with their resentment at being treated as a degraded class when they were, to her surprise, nearly as white of skin as herself and far more richly dressed. But how was she going to be able to appeal to them?

Particularly did she feel uneasy about the large girl with the mischievous eyes, who was half rising to look around at her grinning friends.

"God created each of you equal to anybody," Emily began in a firm voice, "yet you are not treated as equal. I wish to tell you of a secret I learned when I was young." Here she paused impressively. "That secret is that *knowledge is power*. With that power, you can prove you are in no way inferior."

Her eye fell upon the mischievous girl, who had sunk back in her seat and was watching with her mouth agape. To her Emily said, "What is thy name, please?"

"Cleo...ah...Cleo Jones."

"Very well, Cleo Jones. I wish to make a bargain with you young women. If each of you will do your utmost to learn and to better yourselves, I will promise to do my utmost to help you to rise. Does thou not think that is a fair bargain, Cleo?"

Cleo gazed at her so long and searchingly, Emily began to wonder if she was refusing to answer. Finally the girl said wonderingly, "No one ever talked like this to us before." And when there was a giggle at the table behind her, Cleo turned around and, with a look, quelled the offender.

Miss Emily, as the girls called her, was the first teacher to have no "testing" on her opening day, but her sincere concern for their advancement had caught their imaginations. As the term went on, they found out that she meant just what she said. One day, she pointed out, "When some are noisy and quarrelsome, the others cannot study."

Cleo challenged her. "Don't you have to make us mind?"

"Now consider, Cleo. Spread here like a banquet are the subjects you girls need to master to raise your places in this world. If you are hungry for equality, need I force you to eat?"

The girls took home the news of this teacher and her bargain, of course, and soon Miss Miner's school held thirty pupils and the day's schedule was bursting with two dozen recitations for girls of all ages in their various subjects.

Emily stood in the schoolhouse door at the end of the second week, watching them off across the commons. It flashed into her mind that, for the first time in her life, she was using her energy and her abilities to the fullest. At last she was making a difference. In that exquisite moment of realization she stretched her arms wide.

"Are you tired?" inquired Miss Miner, from behind her. "You are working very well, I must say." And later, in their kitchen, she exclaimed, "I am thankful you can cook. It is a relief all around that you are able to take hold like this."

Miss Miner was going to be easy to please, since brown bread and baked beans and coffee suited her as well as more elaborate dishes. In fact, she didn't notice the difference. In her single-minded determination to educate these young women as broadly as possible, she talked through their Spartan meals about her plans, without attending at all to what she was eating. Emily thought it an important part of her job to feed the thin body housing that eager, burning spirit.

Gratified at her praise, Emily now asked, "How did thee come to start this school?"

Miss Miner's face clouded. "I would have thought your friends who told you about this position might have told you all that."

Seeing her injured vanity, Emily was sorry, for she admired the little lady very much.

Miss Miner, however, plunged into her story. "When I was teaching in Mississippi, I saw the wretchedness of the slaves and said I should like to teach them. That planter told me arrogantly that it was a crime to teach a Negro to read. Well, I could do nothing for those miserable people, but I vowed I would later. And where could there be a better place than Washington to demonstrate to visitors from all over the country that these girls can rise through education the same as their pale sisters? Why, do you realize," she declared proudly, "that six of my graduates are conducting their own schools for Negroes this very year?"

"That must be wonderfully gratifying to thee," Emily said earnestly. "It has not been easy for thee, has it?"

"They drove me out of three neighborhoods right here in Washington, by threatening to burn my schools down. I held them off once by waving a pistol!"

Awed, Emily asked, "Was it loaded?"

"No, but they were not to know that. So far out of town as we are here, I keep hoping we may be safe from all that now." Glancing out of the window, however, she said fearfully, "Oh look, there are those white ruffians again! They get a little bolder every day and they terrify the girls. I just do not know what they may do next."

It became clear on Monday morning that the gang hanging around the commons intended to make mischief.

Two of the littler girls came in crying because the boys had snatched and thrown their books and they had been afraid to get close enough to rescue them. Several of the older girls had been pushed off the board walk into the mud, as well. Miss Miner began to fuss, "Oh dear, whatever may they do this afternoon?"

Emily said calmly, "I think we can deal with them when the time comes. Come now, girls, let us commence our work."

At intervals during the day Miss Miner looked out, becoming more and more perturbed as the young fellows gathered. Emily had her hands too full with her many recitations to keep watch, but in the back of her mind she had laid a plan.

By closing time, there were about twenty young men outside the yard. Emily lined up the girls at the door and said, "Now girls, you have heard it said a dog knows if you are afraid and that is when he bites. This is true of bullies, too. While I go out and talk with them, I want you to walk quietly past us in a close group, without running or showing any fear."

Emily smiled encouragingly at the girls, then putting on an air of confidence, swung down the walk. Facing the boys, she introduced herself and then asked pleasantly, "What do you young men do?" She looked from one to another and then at the apparent ringleader. "What about thee?"

He shrugged and shifted his feet. Behind him, the others craned their necks to see her, and one growled, "He don't do nuthin'."

She nodded gravely. "I'm sure you have all discovered that you have to make yourselves fit if you are to gain the position you wish in this world." Out of the corner of her eye she spied the last of the girls silently filing behind the group, and hurried into speech. "I wish each one of you may prepare yourself for the work you could do well and at which you could prosper."

Under their intent eyes, and as the last girl disappeared over the edge of the commons, she declared, "These young women are going to get an education somehow, no matter what difficulties are thrown in their way. They are going to elevate themselves to equal the competence of the best whites. And if you young men do not wish to find yourselves in a position inferior to theirs, you had better be busy with your own educations, and apply yourselves to your books."

Suddenly, one shouted from the rear, "Here, those girls got away!" and they took to their heels across the commons, yelling with rage.

Miss Miner, cowering in the doorway, quavered, "How did you dare go out there to talk to those ruffians?"

"Well, I have brothers, Miss Miner. I expect all boys are pretty much alike."

"Oh, what will they do tomorrow?" fussed Miss Miner, twisting her hands together.

"I hope they may busy themselves more profitably than tormenting these girls, but I do not know that." She was not nearly as cool as her words, for what if her trick had made them revengeful?

The next day, to the relief of all, the gang did not reappear, and Miss Miner repeated her amazement each day that they never bothered the girls again. However, she became more nervous and exhausted as the fall term wore on, and Emily finally suggested that she take on another teacher.

"An excellent idea if you can find a good person."

"I had in mind promoting Emma Brown, Miss Miner. She has been very capable in helping me hear the recitations of the younger girls."

Myrtilla Miner had been glancing over the papers on the desk but at this her head snapped around. "Emma Brown! Don't you realize she is a Negro?"

Emily said gently, "She is competent to do the work, I believe."

"Nonsense! You must have a second white woman in case of any rioting or trouble." Miss Miner's voice was rising. "A colored person can't testify in court."

"Well, we will see what we can do," soothed Emily.

"If you had a good white woman I could get away for a rest."

Once the subject had arisen, Miss Miner began hoping and then planning to take a few months away from the school, to rest and to solicit funds. On the morning she left, Emma Brown carried one of Miss Miner's satchels out to the carriage drawn up at the gate and earnestly assured her, "Miss Miner, you need not worry. Miss Howland never has any trouble with the school." Emily, emerging from the doorway behind them, saw the venomous flash of Miss Miner's eyes as she stepped up into the carriage.

In parting, she commanded, "Now I want you to find a second white teacher."

"I will remember what thee has said, Miss Miner."

The carriage rumbled away in a cloud of dust and the two women sighed in relief. Then catching each other's eyes, they smiled ruefully.

Miss Brown inquired shyly, "Have you a teacher in mind?"

Emily's eyes sparkled. "I have thee in mind. I must run this school with a teacher I know is competent. Miss Miner has been very nervous this fall, but I am sure in the spring when she sees how prosperously we have fared, she will admit I could have done no better."

Emily, comfortable in this belief, took enthusiastic charge of the school, and Emma Brown remained her able assistant and friend.

It was not all pleasantness, of course. There were angry looks from some of the neighbors, and one night vandals threw rocks at the building. Emily also had not forgotten how Miss Miner had been threatened with fire. But she must not dwell on their defenselessness.

Before long, classes expanded into the kitchen of the schoolhouse, and the morning came when Miss Brown called to Emily, "What shall we do? We have no chairs for these two new girls."

"Tell them they must each bring a seat of some kind, if it is only a wooden box."

Miss Miner might be an unpredictable director, but she had been a creative teacher, encouraging the girls to grow flower gardens, to study the stars and to practice composition by writing to prominent figures. She also had scheduled lectures by visiting scholars. Emily felt fortunate to follow in her shoes.

With so much to do, she was cross at catching the measles from one of her girls and wrote to Hannah:

February 26 1858

I have thought a good deal about you in this my spare time of which I am heartily tired. Oh, I am of no more value in a quiet life than a bell never suffered to ring...a great dangling thing of no sort of use.

Once well and back at work, and in her pleasure and satisfaction in the school, Emily had scarcely thought of home. Suddenly it came to her: *Why, Father and Mother are moving up onto the Stage Road, into Judge Sherwood's house.*

She could see in her mind's eye the spacious new house and grounds. Was there a good place in any of the buildings to hide runaway slaves? Never mind, her menfolk had made it clear that was none of her business.

Washington, Apr 4 1858
Dear Mother,

I fancy you are almost in the new house now; how strange it seems that we immovable folk should get moved once in our lives. I hope Ben is with you, he is such a capital helper.

Here she stopped and frowned, thinking of Ben and the girl he had chosen for his bride—a pretty creature with a playful manner. Emily had never cared for the woman, but had scolded herself that doubtless no female would be good enough, in her eyes, for Ben.

After their wedding back in January, a cousin had written her blithely:

Boys should marry. Nothing like it to make them of some consequence in the world.

Well, perhaps so, but she cared more for his happiness than his consequence. Even then, she had not felt at all easy about Ben's choice. Well, she must just hope it might prove to be a felicitous union. Shaking her head doubtfully, she continued writing her letter to Mother.

Last week we had an abundance of company at the school. I was about closing up when the door opened & there stood Dr. Underhill peering thru his spectacles. I showed off the school until the girls were tired of singing & everything else.

After a time he departed. I think, could he hear the girls
call him "that old gentleman who looked over and under
his specs," he would not feel much flattered. He talked
about the degrees of white blood which don't suit their
taste much, right before them.

Farewell, Emily

The tiresome old doctor was not their only visitor. Though their neighbors might hate the school, liberal Northerners considered it a showplace and frequently a senator and his wife might come to call.

Emily concealed her irritation with difficulty at one of these calls. After the senator praised the quality and scope of the girls' work, his wife sweetly explained it away, saying, "But of course they aren't full Negroes." Just as though the white portion of her girls held all their virtue and brains! The visits of school trustee Samuel Bowen and his wife were more welcome, and because they were also Friends and abolitionists, the three found many mutual interests. The Bowens invited her to dinner once, and then again and again, often in a small circle of friends, all of whom took an interest in her work with the colored people.

One evening toward spring, the Sewards, Breeds and Danas were also present. The women had held a sewing bee in the afternoon and the gentlemen had now joined them for dinner. Emily wondered if this quiet group was exactly to the senator's taste, but he was drawn in by his wife's deep interest in helping the poor people of Washington.

Samuel Bowen drew Emily aside and spoke quietly to her. "I must tell thee that I wrote a note to Miss Miner praising thy work and that of Miss Brown. I have had this day a very strange letter in reply, accusing thee of defying her orders."

"In truth," nodded Emily, "I have ignored one order, to hire a white teacher in Emma Brown's stead. She is all I could wish for as assistant and as friend, and she understands the problems of these girls as no white person can. Even so, if the trustees also want a second white teacher, I will comply."

Samuel Bowen shook his head. "With the fine work being done at the school this winter, I could not advise any change."

Emily added, "Miss Miner is also angry with me because the janitor and I painted the schoolhouse. She wrote to ask how we can command any respect for the school when I have set such an unwomanly example. I did not think of it that way, merely how dingy the building looked."

Mrs. Bowen, at her elbow, exclaimed warmly, "It was a fine idea! Emma Brown tells me the girls and their families are all set up about their handsome school. It looks delightful sitting up on the hill in its sparkling new coat. And *I* have heard nothing of its being unsuitable employment for thee."

Dr. Breed added, smiling kindly at her, "And when the enrollment has more than doubled, I can not imagine criticizing our teacher."

Emily looked around the circle of friendly faces, the Bowens, Senator and Mrs. Seward, Dr. and Mrs. Breed and the Danas. Hesitantly, she said, "Your friendship and appreciation is very pleasant to me, but you must realize I may not speak against my employer, even though you be my friends."

Major Dana was a big, kind, brotherly creature who always appeared indulgently amused by her enthusiasm. Here he said lazily, "You are right, of course. Now let me see." And with a teasing smile, "Shall we quarrel about what would happen if slavery were outlawed? How would the freed people support themselves?"

Emily entered into the lively discussion, stoutly declaring to the circle of men, "Judging from my own experience, freedom is at first painful to one who has always been dependent, but surely freedom is worth suffering for!" She had then glanced about to see Mrs. Seward, Mrs. Dana and her hostess laying further plans for the relief of the needy, but here diverted by and smiling at her vehemence. She felt warmed by their affection and approval.

Before the evening was over, Mrs. Seward made an opportunity to say quietly to her, "I think well of what your school is doing for those girls, Emily. It would give me satisfaction to donate a sum toward books." And true to her word, Mrs. Seward became a generous patron of Miner Normal School.

Emily was excited at receiving two cheques for the school from Harriet Beecher Stowe. After all, these sums were raised from the sales of that wonderful book, *Uncle Tom's Cabin*!

Unfortunately, though Miss Miner knew Emily and Miss Brown were an excellent working team, she had no sooner stepped from the carriage on her return in the spring than she snapped, "I see you still have not obeyed my order!"

Emily soothed, "We have been so busy there has been scarce time to think of it, and I knew thee was returning soon. I think a friend from home will come for the fall term, if thee wishes."

"Well, see that you do something about it!"

Miss Brown came out on the steps to greet Miss Miner, whose angry glance included her. "This is my school, and do you not forget it! I can let you both go at the end of the month."

Dismayed, Emily ventured, "Does thee want us to go?"

Miss Miner's eyes slid sideways and she straightened her hat with an irritable jerk. "Oh, I suppose not. But just you remember whose school it is."

Emily and Miss Brown exchanged uneasy glances as they followed her in, but having vented her resentment, Miss Miner approved the class work. Even so, both Emily and Miss Brown knew that a second white teacher must be on hand at the opening of the fall term.

"You won't be needing me next term," Emma said, trying to hide her chagrin.

"Indeed, we shall need thee, no matter who else is here," said Emily stoutly. "Thee is a fine teacher and it galls me that thee cannot have thy proper chance. Thee should have thine own school and if only I had independent means, I would help thee to prepare thyself for it." Then looking at Emma's grateful face, she chuckled. "Thee need not thank me for what I cannot do for thee."

"You think I could someday have my own school?" marveled Emma, her face ashine.

"Does thee not feel thyself to be a good teacher and competent to be a headmistress?"

"Yes, I do, but then when I hear Miss Miner...."

"Miss Miner indeed! We need pay no attention to her opinion on this point, for she will never be able to recognize ability in a colored skin. That does not mean that many others cannot."

Emma smiled and then bent her head over the papers she had been correcting. Suddenly, she looked up and announced, "One day I *shall* have my own school!"

Emily smiled proudly at the girl and said warmly, "I know thee will!"

However, that day was far in the future, so when Emily came back from her summer spent at home in Sherwood's Corners, she brought with her an enthusiastic and competent teacher in her friend, Ann Searing. Surely, this would heal the ill feelings of Miss Miner.

Before she had even set foot in the schoolhouse, she knew herself mistaken. Some of the girls could not wait until school opened to greet their teachers, but had followed the carriage up the hill. They clustered about as Emily and Ann Searing were ready to step down, and in the forefront, as always, was Cleo Jones, smiling broadly.

Miss Miner came out on the step and said sharply, "Here, step back. And *you*, what are you staring at?"

Cleo answered happily, "I'm just glad to see Miss Emily. She's...she's so good!"

Emily saw rather than heard the exchange, but she also saw Miss Miner turning her shoulder to Cleo and shooting an angry look at Emily herself. She entered the schoolhouse with a sinking heart.

To her gratification, the fall term opened with sixty students. Ann Searing worked as earnestly for their betterment as Emily and Emma Brown, who was now their assistant. Often the three of them shook their heads over Miss Miner's unpredictable ways. To their relief, she took her sharp looks and her crotchets off on another rest and fund-raising tour over the winter and left them to their work.

> *Washington, Nov 7 1858*
> *My dear Hannah*
>
> *The school is finely started. Ann Searing fits in exactly and I think we work together as well as I could wish. I wrote Ben last week enclosing directions for my apples & butter. I would be glad if some lard could be put in the barrel of apples. Grease seems to be a very difficult matter here. We live on sweet potatoes mostly...*

During the winter, when the attention of the young women in her class began to flag, she suddenly demanded, "Have you girls read *Uncle Tom's Cabin?*"

"We don't need to read that. *We* are free!" declared one.

"You are right, you are in no peril. You are too comfortable altogether. After the desperate risks some of my dark friends have taken, I compare them to you careless girls wasting your opportunities and burn to give you a vision of what you can do.

"I see you idling away your lives, chasing shadows. Riches and fine clothes cannot yield an iota of happiness to your souls. I want to see you learn to do and *give*."

Looking at their jaded faces, she urged, "Wake up to your responsibility to your race! On you depends the future of four million people! If I were in your place, I would prove that my mental powers are equal to those of whiter skins. I should make it so clear that none need inquire."

Perhaps they had caught a bit of her vision; perhaps they merely wished to hear no more of her harangue. In any case, they all settled in and worked much harder that week.

Satisfied though she was with the girls' progress, Emily was uneasy about the future of this school. Samuel Bowen asked her to meet with the trustees at his house one evening. As she looked about at the gloomy faces, she realized she was not alone in her fears.

One trustee asked, "What is this plan of hers for an elaborate new building when she can hardly find funds enough for the old one?"

A sensible-appearing man across from Emily said, "I, for one, will not continue to give funds to a woman that I think is losing her reason."

In the serious discussion that followed this declaration, Mr. Bowen nodded at Emily and she slipped away to join Mrs. Bowen in her private sitting room, while the voices grew louder.

"Emily dear, this evening is not so pleasant as our usual gathering of friends, is it?" asked Mrs. Bowen. "Samuel worries about thy employer. She is an odd woman. Does she worry thee?"

To this discreet friend, Emily disclosed, "She changes as the weather! Last week she wrote me to press on with the work and try to gain more students, and thee knows, Mrs. Bowen, that we are pushing the walls out now. Then yesterday I received a scold from her that I forget whose school it is and take too much on myself."

"Samuel is anxious to know how thee is paying the school bills. He says she left thee short of funds."

Emily smiled shamefacedly. "Well, to speak the truth, I am using my own money. The place never pays for itself in winter, but in the spring the tuition money will come in and then I will reimburse myself."

In the spring, however, a jealous Miss Miner came back acting more erratic than ever, and the incredulous young women soon found themselves dismissed. Emily appealed to her father:

> She goes and hires a teacher and tells the scholars that she shall take the school the first of next month, without saying a word to us! Now I am obliged to accept thy offer and suppose I shall need thirty dollars to get home.

It was bitterly hard to say good-bye to her girls but she reminded them, "On you depends the emancipation of your race. Use your intellects to shame your oppressors!"

The first shock of dismissal over, she was still annoyed, upon reaching Sherwood's Corners, to be greeted by Mother's, "Well, it is time thee stayed home, Emily. Thee knows Hannah expects her child anytime, and I have plenty for thee to be doing as well."

The Howlands of
Sherwood, New York:
Quakers, Abolitionists

Slocum Howland
Father
1794–1881

Hannah Tallcot Howland
Mother
1796–1867

Brother
William Howland
1823–1905

Brother
Benjamin Howland
1832–1882

Emily Howland
1827–1929

Emily cared little for Mother's household chores, but to Hannah, who had gone on seeing to Mother, thus enabling Emily to go back to Miss Miner's school for her second year, Emily owed a debt far beyond any help she could offer her now.

Baby Isabel was born in May and she was a most lovable child. Still, though thoroughly ashamed of her own selfishness and most careful to hide her feelings from Hannah, Emily sometimes groaned to herself, "Is this the way I must spend my life when so much elsewhere needs doing?"

Camomile: "Energy in Action"

1859

As Emily took up the reins of the household and waited on her querulous little mother, some of her afternoon callers unintentionally scraped her nerves. One tried to console her, saying, "I never could see thee as a teacher anyway."

Another of Mother's friends went further, however, saying with an aggravating little titter, "I knew thee would get thy comeuppance. I told thee before thee went, woman's place is in the home. And now where will thee find a husband?"

Emily managed to swallow her wrath and make a civil reply, but turned to her diary to pour out her despair:

> *I am a cipher in the world's esteem if I lack a man at my left.*

How hard it was, after earning respect for her work in Washington, to become a naught in Sherwood, as Sherwood's Corners was now called. And all this simply because she had finally and firmly vowed not to marry.

And again she wrote:

> *O Earth, everywhere you put the man, and the woman nowhere. With all my little strength will I fight against this monstrous injustice, this mountain of wrongs crushing down the woman.*

She was able to put aside pricks and snubs when she picked up Hannah's infant. Isabel was surely the most irresistible baby Emily had ever known, with her sweet, sociable little ways, and Emily fell into the habit of spending many hours with her.

Still, she complained to Ben when next she saw him that she felt she *must* do something more, in these times. To her surprise, he immediately said, "Thee can work for me. I need someone honest and capable to keep the factory accounts straight."

She was quick to accept his offer. She could certainly keep accounts, and it would be pleasant to be working with dear Ben. Unfortunately, this required her staying frequently with Ben and his wife, Louise, and her coolness to him now and then cut Emily to the heart.

Well did she remember how, long ago, Ben had run to Mother, crying because he could not go with Father and William. Hand to forehead, she had fretted, "Oh, go along, Benjamin, do! I cannot bother with thy nonsense." He had come to nine-year-old Emily and leaned his head against her shoulder while she put her arms around him.

She had been able to comfort Ben then, but now, close as they were, she could not interfere. She could make his office pleasant, but not his home, and this took much of her pleasure from being with him.

By December she was writing:

Sherwood

Dear Friends,

I spend half my time at my brother's near Auburn to keep books.

This makes me very busy but does not exorcise the demon of unrest who possesses me. I seem to be doomed to grope around never finding my true place.

My sister Hannah and I are each preparing a Christmas tree. She, one for this neighborhood, I, one for the factory children. Every little thing weighs something, I believe, but I work at trifles.

One absorbing interest to Emily was the talk between her father and William of the growing tension between the North and South. Despite her mother's exasperation at her unmaidenliness, she could not stay out of their discussions.

"Father!" Emily heard the front door bang as William burst in. "Father, is thee here? The news is in, and what does thee think?"

Emily threw down her hair brush and rushed to hang over the banister to listen eagerly. They were all avidly awaiting news by the morning stage, of the Republican convention. Though they were almost certain their friend William Seward had been nominated for President, still....

"Sit thee down, William," she heard Father say.

"I can't sit," declared William impatiently. "They've thrown the nomination to a nobody. And Seward had the most votes of any candidate on the first ballot!"

Emily had run down the stairs, tripping over her long skirt, and now caught her balance by clutching her brother's arm. "William, who got it, then?"

Neither of them in their excitement paid heed to Mother's cluck of dismay, "Emily, Emily!"

"Has thee ever heard of a Lincoln from Illinois?"

Father, who had been shaking his head in disappointment, brightened up now. "Lincoln! Why yes, William, and so has thee, for he's spoken out against slavery for years. When he debated Stephen Douglas, he accused slaveowners of demanding, 'You work and toil and earn bread, and I'll eat it.'"

William shrugged. "It was easy to talk then. But now even if he can manage to get himself elected, I suppose he'll have to let slavery spread to the territories to avoid a split."

As soon as Emily could swallow her disappointment over Senator Seward's defeat, she admitted they had misjudged their candidate. Abraham Lincoln might be a nobody, but he was sticking to his antislavery principles.

They debated, there in Sherwood in 1860, whether he or any president could hold the United States together now. William pointed out to his father and Emily when he brought in the newspaper one evening, "The Southerners are saying, 'Your Northern high-mindedness about our slaves costs you nothing. If they go free, your economy won't go to smash from loss of cheap labor. You won't have to live with them if they take to looting for a living.' They are saying they can't afford our scruples."

Father leaned his chin on his hand thoughtfully.

Emily said hotly, "They do not admit it is intolerable human exploitation!"

William said mildly, "They can't afford to admit that, Emily."

During the campaigning, the country trembled on the brink of war. When the South, defeated on Election Day, declared it was seceding and war soon followed, Emily became more and more restless.

One evening she burst out, "Father, I cannot bear being idle when there is such need! We say our Army rescues the slaves, but is it a rescue when they leave homes and regular meals to tag along behind the Union lines, with no provision made for them? Let me read thee this letter from Mrs. Breed. Or here, read it thyself."

She shoved the letter into his hands but went on excitedly, "She says nearly a thousand of the poor wretches have straggled into Washington. They're living in a makeshift camp under horrible conditions. My friend, Dr. Breed, is surgeon at a camp hospital for the poor souls, does thee know?"

Father lowered the close-written sheets and looked calmly over his spectacles at her. "Now Emily, I shall do better if thee will permit me to read it myself."

They rejoiced, in the autumn of 1862, at Abraham Lincoln's proclamation freeing the slaves on the first of January next. And Emily relished Harriet Beecher Stowe's visit to Washington to make sure of the president's signing it, so it would not "fizzle out of the little end of the powder horn."

Escorted to Lincoln's study, so the newspaper said, Mrs. Stowe had watched as Lincoln unfolded himself from a chair to tower over her. Putting out his huge hand to take hers, he had remarked, "So this is the little lady who made this big war."

Father, laying aside the paper, commented, "Mrs. Stowe imagines the war will be over the minute the slaves are free. She doesn't see that Lincoln intends to force the South back into the Union first."

William said, "Or that thousands who can't escape from their masters may still be slaves."

Emily added anxiously, "She doesn't know that the ones who've been freed are worse off than before, with no way to support themselves. Mrs. Breed writes that their conditions in that Washington camp are frightful."

1863

And frightful it was, beyond anything Emily had imagined, when she arrived to work at the Freedmen's Camp on the northern outskirts of Washington, on a bleak January day. Forgotten were her mother's sighs and her father's encouragement. Forgotten was the long journey on trains crowded with inductees and with servicemen invalided home. Forgotten was all but this incredible scene.

"I did warn you it was dreadful, did I not?" asked Mrs. Breed.

Emily did not answer. Her horrified eyes were flying, from the open field, a sea of mud—to the buildings converted from old barracks and stables, and the sodden tents made of quilts—to the gaunt ragged people milling about everywhere. And oh, there was a man with a foot off, using two sticks to walk. And oh mercy! Here was a strapping ebony-skinned man helping to unload Mrs. Breed's supplies from the wagon, and he had a brand burned on his forehead!

Guilemia Breed took her arm. "Come Emily, help me to hand out these clothes. I know they need stockings and blankets in that second shack."

To be busy, Emily found, conquered the horror. Even finding a dozen people packed into the dark, stinking hovel and an old granny curled up on a bed of ragged clothes on the dirt floor, who whispered, "I's dying, I guess,"—even discovering there was "No water today, missy" to cool the poor old woman's fevered face and hands— it was all bearable, if she could work toward making it better.

And work she did.

The days ran into weeks while she turned beggar, writing home, writing her Philadelphia friends, writing every society or agency she had ever heard of:

> Send food...dried fruit...cheese...send clothes...patching scraps... blankets... flannel to wrap the babies in...calico for frocks...old bonnet frames for the aunties to recover...warm stockings and knit them large... and, oh yes, an umbrella, please!

She found herself tending the dying, doling out quinine to the feverish, laudanum to the pain-wracked, morphine for the hopeless, kerosene or skunk oil to rub on congested chests, boiled onions for poultices. And teaching any women who were healthy enough to mend and to sew garments which she cut out for them. And unpacking and distributing the contents of the parcels that flooded in from Northerners who had been stirred by her pleas.

Rushed as she was, it was vital that she write home:

> March 31 1863
> My dear Mother,
>
> I am sorry that thee has had any anxiety about my health when the truth was I was so very well. The smallpox has been prevalent but is diminishing rapidly. The smallpox patients are in a hospital at some distance from the camp. So dismiss all fears. I never felt so well anywhere, as here.

This was all very well to soothe Mother, but Emily had in fact dealt with a few sufferers from the dreaded pox. She was thankful she had not taken the infection, for they could ill afford to spare her efforts.

May 7 1863

I suppose the time which I proposed staying here is about expired. I feel as tho' I had just learned how to work with some efficiency. I will come home if you say so, but if there is no suffering need of me there, I know there is here. I would like to have a longer leave of absence here in this hour of our country's & humanity's great need. We have several northeast storms every week. They have made it very hard for our poor dwellers in tents and the little children fare but poorly. I always dread to make my round of visits the morning following a storm. Beds of rags all wet, the poor little things stowed away under them.

Emily now heard from home that Hermon Phillips, the fugitive slave whom her father had ransomed and settled in Sherwood, had insisted on sending all three of his strapping sons in a regiment of colored volunteers. Hermon said if they failed to do their duty he would go down himself, for he had an old score to settle with the South.

This brave man had risked a long and fearsome trek north, with dangers at every turn, to save his first two bright, handsome lads. And yet, for this cause of freedom, he was willingly risking his sons!

Emily folded up the letter wonderingly, and then turned back to her work.

The weeks ran on and she began to know these people well and to become particularly fond of some of them.

Especially there was Ella, the appealingly beautiful young girl who had arrived at the Freedmen's Camp with her husband, Lewis Carter. He carried their infant son, while a little girl clung to her mother's skirt. Looking around at the mud and shacks, Ella had said laughingly to Emily, "This minds me of my auntie's saying, 'I's halfway between Thank God and O Lord!' But pay that no mind, we's free now!"

And when Emily offered a change of clothes, Ella had quickly said, "We'll get along. We don't need help. We's willing to work."

Certainly both of them proved to be very willing to work, but it was Ella who most delighted Emily. The girl sang in the field and cheerfully waved and smiled whenever she saw Emily passing.

Though she looked to be less than half the age of her husband and too young to be a mother, she was working as hard as any man. Emily would have pitied her except that she was always so sunny.

Many other families were not faring as well, however, and Emily discovered that the surly camp superintendent was at the bottom of most of their woes.

"Mr. Nichols," she pleaded, "we've got to have more food rations. These people are starving."

"Let them work, then."

"According to my calculations, they are not getting their fair wages from thee when they do work. How are they to pay six dollars a month rent and get anything to eat, when thee does not pay them?"

His eyes flashed angrily. "There isn't money enough for charity. They work or they starve."

She could not budge him from this position. Part of his rage, no doubt, was because she, a woman, was daring to check on him. But was he also skimming off some of the money that was rightfully theirs?

Suspicion turned to certainty when Ella sought her out at week's end to ask, "Miss Emily, how many hours are eight and eight and eight?"

"Twenty-four, Ella."

"That Nichols! He told me eighteen!"

When Emily interceded, Nichols, with an ugly look, snarled, "That jade accuses me of cheating? The poor fool can't add. She worked six hours on three days and that's all I'll pay her for."

Emily had to report back to Ella, "It is thy word against his and since thee has no proof, I can't make him change. I do want to get a school started here and when I can do that, I think thee should come."

Ella was much taken with this idea. "Oh, I would cer'nly like to be able to add up my hours."

"Yes, and to read," said Emily, "so thee can see what he writes down."

Ella shot her a startled look and then declared, "When you starts your school, I'll be there."

At present, however, there was no time for school. Emily was far too busy trying to fill the barest needs of the newcomers, with Nichols taking enjoyment from hampering her efforts.

On the worst morning of all, she rose and dressed wearily, well after her usual hour. Each time she had closed her eyes during the night, she had remembered Nichols' triumphant smirk as he once again refused her a burial permit. Each time, she had flung herself over on her narrow cot, and each time the slats became more evident through her thin straw mattress.

Poor old Granny Clay was now four days dead and her family was frantic. If Emily could not somehow get that permit from Nichols, she might better be packing, for her usefulness was over. The man would now deliberately thwart her on every request.

During her morning round of calls, she heard wagon wheels. Listlessly, she went to the door. Then seeing the driver, she cried impulsively, "Uncle Moses! Is thee going in to town?"

"Yes, miss," nodded the gentle black giant. "I's to get the bread ration for camp."

"Wait for me!" She had just one thought, and that the comfort of Frances Seward's presence. Calling a hasty farewell to the family she was leaving, she rushed out and clambered up beside him in the big, clumsy wagon.

Uncle Moses' sad strong face had long interested Emily. On any other day, as they clopped along into Washington, she would have asked to hear his story of the troubles and sorrows which had carved those lines of suffering. Today, however, she slumped beside him, silent and disheartened.

At last he said, "'Pears like you's mighty low today, Miss Emily." Looking at her with deep, kind eyes, he added, "It's that man Nichols, ain't it? He's a bad man, the way he treats us all."

Emily felt warmed by his understanding. Uncle Moses, if she could manage to survive here at all, would be a friend worth knowing better.

As he pulled his team into the long bakery line at the Capitol building, she jumped down and explained where Mrs. Seward lived. Then she asked dubiously, "Will thee be able to fetch me when thee finishes the errands?"

With a broad smile he assured her, "I's glad to do that for you, Miss Emily."

In her haste and single-minded need to reach Mrs. Seward, she had not given a thought to how dreary and odd her work clothes, without fashionable hoop or stiff crinoline, would appear here. Nor had she expected these congested, noisy streets in the heart of the city, so different from the quieter days when she was here at Miss Miner's.

Hurrying along, she found herself meeting a company of soldiers, marching in ragged formation from the direction of the Union Depot. Some wore an assortment of smart new blue uniforms; others wore their own drab, rumpled clothes.

"Compane-ee, halt! At ease!"

As the men lifted awed faces to the Capitol building, she had to pass alongside them. She heard a countryman exclaim, "I wish Mary Jane could see this house of Congress. She would not wonder then that our taxes are so enormous."

Stealing a look at his thin, anxious face, she caught his eye. Before she could look away, he suddenly blurted in kindly concern, "Oh ma'am, this is no place for you, a woman alone."

Gratefully, she murmured, "I know, private, but I've only a bit further to go now."

It might not be so very far from the Capitol to the White House along Pennsylvania Avenue, and from there only a very short walk to the Seward home. Nevertheless, the walking was nearly impossible, for there in her path was a horse-drawn streetcar, pulled over to let another marching company past. Surely these men were battle veterans, for they looked drawn and jaded, in their worn and faded uniforms. And here were pedestrians waiting to make their way across the avenue through the crush of carriages and marching troops.

The kindly private was right, this was a dangerous place, though not in the way he meant. Once she had to leap back from the wheels of a wagon which she had not heard above the din. To the soldiers, however, she was invisible in her drab clothes.

She only wished she were as unnoticed by the stylish women, swaying about in their graceful bell-shaped skirts. How mortifying it was to feel their sideways glances of scorn or amusement at her limp skirts and bonnet, draggled from all the drizzles and downpours. And when she caught her toe on a tree root, ripping loose the stitches holding the sole of her heavy work shoe and barely catching herself from pitching headlong, she groaned aloud. With no string to tie around her shoe to stop the flapping, she must lift her foot high at every step and slap it down to keep from tripping again. She pulled her bonnet brim lower over her burning face. What an object of hilarity she must appear!

And, to add to her misery, the closer she came to the White House, the worse the stench became. She had thought nothing could reek worse than the camp, but here the fumes were nearly overpowering, from the open latrines of all these soldiers and also from the sluggish canal, fouled with blood from the Army's slaughter of animals. To her horror, though she was breathing through her mouth, waves of nausea swept over her.

Never had she been so thankful to reach haven as when she rang Mrs. Seward's bell. She was sure the maid, at first glance, thought she was a beggar woman. Once Emily reached Mrs. Seward's cozy sitting room, her chagrin melted under the warmth of her welcome.

Frances Seward laid aside a sheaf of papers to rise quickly and take Emily's hand. She immediately called for tea and bread and butter. Upon coaxing forth Emily's story of frustration, she sent the maid back for cold meat, applesauce and sponge cake as well, saying affectionately that her young friend looked half-starving.

As Emily ate, nibbling cautiously at first and then simply trying not to wolf the delicious food, Mrs. Seward sat, pursing her lips thoughtfully. Finally, she said with decision, "I'm going to keep you here today. Did you come in with the camp wagon?"

"Yes, with Uncle Moses Washington. He's waiting in the line at the bakery in the Capitol building."

"Then my boy can find him and tell him you're staying here and we will send you back in the carriage tonight." Mrs. Seward rose and rustled out of the room.

Emily called after her, "He must look for the tallest, broadest black man with snow white hair." Then she leaned her head back. This house was an oasis of gracious order in a town turned upside down. And how grateful she was that Uncle Moses would not need to pilot that huge awkward rig through these swarming streets.

Frances Seward (1805–1865), wife of Lincoln's
Secretary of State, William Seward, and Emily's mentor.

Mrs. Seward returned several minutes later to report, "Cicero is running down the avenue. And now you are going straight upstairs to get into a hot bath. The maids are pouring it right now. And then you shall have a nap, for you are tired out."

"A real bath!" The very prospect gave Emily's trembling knees the strength to climb the stairs. When she eased herself blissfully into the nearly scalding water, nothing else mattered, not even that the black hand that set another steaming jug around the edge of the screen was also taking her clothes off the top of it.

When she finally emerged and peered around the screen, she found a towel and a warm robe as well. Wrapped in this, she fell on the bed, pulled up the coverlet and sank gratefully into oblivion.

Hours later, she roused to see a smiling maid bearing her clothes, clean and pressed.

"Oh, how kind!" Emily said, warmly.

"Miz Seward says ain't no hurry, miss. Supper's in half an hour."

Nevertheless, feeling fully revived, Emily scrambled back into her clothes. Reaching for her shoes, she discovered the flapping sole had been expertly cobbled. Was there no end to the kindness of her hostess?

Hurrying downstairs, she exclaimed, as she reentered Mrs. Seward's pretty sitting room, "A real bath and a real bed, and my apparel all refurbished! I am a new woman."

Her hostess again laid aside the sheaf of papers and smiled warmly up at her.

"Am I interrupting thy work?"

"Well, let me pour you a cup of tea. Then if you will not mind, I do wish to finish this summary before Henry comes in, for he needs to see it before his meeting tonight."

Emily would not allow herself to show curiosity about what Mrs. Seward was busily writing, so she sat down where she could look out the window at the greenery. When had she last enjoyed such a moment of peace?

"There, I think I can do no better," said her hostess at last, laying her work aside with her written sheet on top. "By reading and summarizing these lengthy reports for Henry, I can save him many hours."

Emily smiled to herself at Mrs. Seward's unconscious use of her own private name for her husband, but was very surprised at the work she was doing. Emily, of course, knew by now that Mrs. Seward's shyness prevented her acting as official hostess for her husband.

And Emily had also heard from home that Mrs. Seward was very unwell, suffering grievously from abscessed teeth. She had not expected that a woman, both shy and ill, could be of such use to her husband.

Emily had no time to make any remark, for Secretary Seward came in just then, and though he greeted her pleasantly, his eye went directly to the report.

"Done, are you, my faithful scribe?" Patting Mrs. Seward's shoulder in passing, he took up the handwritten sheet and read it carefully, once pausing and saying, "Aha! How fortunate am I in this gift of yours for nosing out what these committees wrap up and bury in high-sounding words." Finally, looking sharply at his wife, he said ruefully, "Well, I presume I know what you think I should do about this."

"Why, Henry, there is only one right course for you to take."

They looked at each other, she meeting his thoughtful frown with a serenely expectant face.

At last his brow cleared. "Yes, I see how it can be done."

As he laid the report aside, Frances Seward enquired, "And haven't you something for us?"

He slapped his breast pocket. "Oh, yes," and drawing out a folded paper, he handed it to his wife. Opening it eagerly and scanning it, she handed it in turn to her guest. "Is that what you need?"

Before Emily's incredulous eyes was a dated order for a burial permit for Sarah Clay, deceased four days since, with a space for the signature of a colonel at the War Office. She gazed at Mr. Seward, speechlessly.

He remarked carelessly, "That is only the rough copy, of course. Nichols received the signed original hours ago." With a grin he added, "If a mere colonel does not intimidate this man Nichols, then we'll go higher." Here he smiled teasingly at his wife, "But I never waste cannonballs where bird shot will do."

"Oh, Henry," protested Mrs. Seward, returning his smile reluctantly. "Such an expression!"

Seeing Emily joyfully rereading the order to Nichols, Mrs. Seward asked, "Will you help with the burial arrangements, I expect?"

Secretary Seward cut in, "She doesn't want to deal with burials."

Emily answered firmly, "It must be done and I will do it."

Shaking his head wonderingly, Seward looked from one face to the other. "You are a pair, aren't you?"

Fanny Seward's presence at dinner completed Emily's pleasure in the day, for they had always been fond of each other. The younger woman's admiring interest in Emily's work and indifference to her unfashionable attire banished any lingering chagrin of the morning.

Emily had begun to discount the reports of Mrs. Seward's poor health as ill founded, until that lady unfortunately craved a taste of the pudding with a browned sugar sauce.

"Oh Mother, you shouldn't eat that," breathed Fanny and hastily explained to Emily, "Sweets aggravate poor Mother's teeth."

Even Seward put down his spoon and watched anxiously.

"Oh, how good that was," Mrs. Seward exclaimed and, looking at her family, she added smiling, "There, you see it's all right." Then doubt crossed her face. By the time her face had drawn with pain, Seward had already leaped to the bell and rung for her maid. Striding to the door, he sharply ordered, "Fetch the laudanum for your mistress."

Then urgently, half-lifting Mrs. Seward, he said, "Come rinse your mouth, my dear."

"So foolish of me," she breathed. "I knew better, Henry."

One of Emily's sharpest impressions that evening was of a chief advisor to the president of the United States, bending solicitously over his wife and murmuring, "You will be all right if I go to my meeting?"

She was lying back on a chaise and clutching Fanny's hand as she awaited the numbing comfort. Nevertheless, she answered firmly, "You *must* go to your meeting, Henry," and she tried painfully to smile at Emily as Secretary Seward ushered her out of the door.

As he handed Emily up into his carriage, he warned soberly, "It occurs to me that this Nichols may quite likely guess it was through you that his infraction came to official notice." He added slowly, "And he's going to be able to pay you back with a dozen petty difficulties every day."

Raising her chin, Emily declared stoutly, "If I can get the necessities for my people, I can put up with anything for myself."

He shook his head dubiously at that. "Well, we must hope he doesn't see you arriving back at your boarding house in this rig." He raised his hat to her, closed the door, and strolled off to his meeting, as the carriage rolled smoothly away.

Emily leaned forward to peer curiously at the soldiers prowling about the streets, or tending the campfires here and there.

Somehow, though she had heard over and over that Washington was a city at war, she had but recently registered that the enemy capital, Richmond, was only a little more than a hundred miles away, and all between was battleground. This war was close.

Then banishing the war and all else from her head, she leaned back against the deep cushions. She could not remember when she had been so comfortably full of excellent food, so rested, and so warmed with friendship. And with her deadlock with Nichols broken, she felt herself to be a different creature from this morning.

For all that, she did not deceive herself about Nichols; he would have guessed she was behind that order. And if not, the camp had a thousand eyes and, as close by the camp as she lived, someone would be sure to tell him of her return in this fine carriage. That would be all the confirmation he needed.

Sure enough, her eyes fell upon him the next day, watching with an ugly look as she passed with her pitiful little burial party. Even as she nodded civilly, she was wondering what meanness would be next.

She was soon to learn. He was now cutting the water deliveries to the camp so not only were her people dirty, they were actually thirsty. So then she had to approach him again to plead, "Mr. Nichols, thee must have more water hauled in!"

"Can't do that. It would cost too much."

It was no use arguing. This man was perfectly capable of further cutting the loads of water to spite her, even if some poor souls should actually die of dehydration.

She had wandered back to the lot where people with jars and pails were milling aimlessly about the empty water wagons. The military commander of the camp, Captain Ferree, rode by. Seeing her, he wheeled his horse about and dismounted.

"What is the trouble, ma'am?" he asked, looking about at the forlorn freedmen.

"Oh, captain," exclaimed Emily eagerly, "we are so short on water! Some of these people thee sees here have had none for two days. Can thee do anything to get us water?"

"Two days! Has anyone told Nichols of this?"

She lifted distressed eyes to his. "He says it is too expensive to give us what we need."

"Too expensive? The wagons are standing right here, and any one of a dozen of these fellows can drive a team, I daresay. We'll soon sort this out!"

He swung himself back up into the saddle, muttering, "A thousand people and he idles the water wagons!" Then looking down at her with interest, and perhaps some admiration, he assured her, "I'll see that you have water here within an hour or two." Touching his hat brim with his gloved hand, he cantered away.

Even in her relief, she earnestly hoped that she was wrong about the captain's expression. Nothing could be finer than to have him interested in her people, while nothing could be more troublesome than to attract his personal interest.

On her way back to her quarters, she was handed a letter from a friend back in Sherwood: "Thee does not mention teaching."

Teaching! There was no time to think of that, when her every effort went to help these poor wretches merely to survive.

However, by May, a neat little school stood just outside the camp. To her satisfaction, she was teaching short sessions morning and afternoon, and talking of starting evening classes for the adults.

One afternoon as she started home from school, she saw Uncle Moses trying to lift a wheel of his wagon out of the mud. He shouted, "Giddap there!" and gave one powerful heave; the horse lunged and the wagon moved ahead. With a "whoa now," he walked forward to pat the horse's neck and rub his hand over its nose. "Good girl."

Then seeing Emily close by, he hailed her excitedly, all one wide smile. "Miss Emily! Just think of this, when I saw Uncle Sam's rig a-coming today, I couldn't rightly help myself. I ran right out to him and held up my hand, and he told the driver to stop and he leaned down and *shook my hand*! And I said, 'God bless you, Uncle Sam!' and *he* said, 'I thank you, my friend.' Ain't that somethin', *me* and *Uncle Sam!*"

"Oh, that's wonderful," Emily exclaimed and sincerely meant it, for the passing of President Lincoln in his open carriage, flanked by his mounted guards, always excited her, too. When he commuted past the camp to his summer cottage at Soldiers Home, she stood amid the freedmen and gazed at "Uncle Sam" with them.

Now, however, Uncle Moses noticed, "You's looking tired, Miss Emily. Step up and I'll just drop you by home." He wiped his muddy hands on a tuft of grass, then courteously handed her up into the wagon.

As they went along, she told him how Ella, cheated of her rightful pay, planned to come to Emily's evening class to learn to count.

"I 'specs they's cheated me, too. And Ben Tolliver, he says whatever he has to buy at the camp store, they never will tell him how much it costs, and then his pay is short from what he cal'lated."

They clopped along a bit, and then he added, "It all comes back to that Nichols. He better watch his step or I's 'fraid he might wake up dead some morning."

Emily, in sudden alarm, gasped, *"Uncle Moses!"*

He looked at her in surprise, then reassured her, "Oh, not me. I's not a violent man. But he's cheated too many and sometime there'll be a ruckus for sure."

After musing for a few moments, he asked, "You says Ella Carter's going to your school? Wisht I could! I knows a few letters, is all. And I can figger some."

"Why, thee can come, uncle!"

"Oh, I's too old."

"No one is ever too old to go to school," she declared. Uncle Moses did not forget this, and when she opened her night school, it was one of her chief pleasures to see Uncle Moses' snow-white head looming above the dark ones.

However, nursing was needed here as critically as teaching, so Emily had been glad to receive a letter from Cornelia Hancock, who had nursed in an Army hospital at Gettysburg. Miss Hancock, the sister of one of Emily's Philadelphia friends, was volunteering for nursing duty at the Freedmen's Camp, between her stints of army nursing. Emily had hurried to give the letter to Dr. Breed at one of the camp hospitals, and he was looking for Nurse Hancock soon.

New tender feelings toward Emily's colored friends were growing, as she knew them better and better. To her surprise, when Captain Ferree escorted her to watch one of their dances on a moonlit evening, she discovered perhaps she did not know them after all.

Men, women and children had gathered for a grand breakdown, with a banjo, drum and fiddler. Their favorite dance was a sort of basket cotillion, the music being a song.

> *Mas'r had a big, black cat*
> *Go in, go in...*
> *Mas'r had a fine wool hat,*
> *Go in, go in...*
> *Black man had some 'possum fat,*
> *Next go in.*
> *Yellow girl, sweet as honey,*
> *Go in, go in.*
> *Black man do the work and mas'r spend the money,*
> *Next go in.*

Everyone sang and clapped, everyone swayed to the strong beat. At the tapping feet and the rapt expressions on their laughing faces, Emily started back, her hands to her face.

"What is the matter?" asked the captain solicitously.

"I do not know. It is all so strange, so primitive. It almost frightens me!"

She immediately regretted giving voice to this weakness, for Captain Ferree's look of tender indulgence was far from welcome, yet she could hardly rebuff him, since by dealing with Nichols, he alone was enabling her to get back to her usual productive schedule.

And Emily's days were full: unpacking and distributing clothing to the continual arrivals who seemed never to have a change of clothing; cooking up dried fruit to make it stretch further, and doling it out; writing letters of thanks, for the people who had sent these clothes and supplies wanted to hear how they were being used.

And her work was made heavier by having to look the other way when rats lurked and slunk around corners; trying not to listen to the gnawing at night; by breathing through her mouth when the stench of raw sewage got too rank; by either dragging her feet through sticky mud, or else choking on the swirling dust.

Never had she been busier, never in such filthy, reeking, hopeless surroundings, and yet, never happier!

Emily voiced this thought at dinner at the Danas' one evening. She then looked about to catch the eye of Mollie Barlow, an exuberant, beautifully dressed newcomer who had promised, at their first meeting, to help at the Freedmen's camp.

"Just give me time to find the shops and markets," this glowing young woman had said, "and to make brother Claude's military quarters habitable. Then I shall join you!"

The inevitable questions, that first evening, had called forth an infectious laugh. "Oh, they give their officers about three horrid chairs and a table in the parlor. And Claude and I have a bed apiece, each hard as the floor, in a couple of little cells. But you ladies wait and see what I shall do with lace curtains, a few lengths of damask, and a brave show of pictures and china. You will admit we have the most elegant drawing room in the city!"

Emily had fully believed this laughing, high-spirited girl could do all she said. And Mrs. Dana had later congratulated Emily on gaining such a helper, saying not only was Miss Barlow good-hearted and energetic, but she had an independent fortune, some of which might help supply the most burning needs at the camp.

And tonight, Mrs. Dana had muttered, "Perchance you can divert some of the funds that girl spends on those gowns of hers to replace the rags on your old aunties."

On the contrary, before the ladies ever rose from the table, Emily knew what Mollie was going to tell her when they sat down together in the drawing room.

"When last we talked, I did fully intend to join in your work, Miss Howland, and I still feel much interest, but...." Mollie shook her head soberly.

Emily's eyes danced. "Ah, yes, I know the signs. I had already gathered that thy main interest now centers in the young lieutenant whom I met at dinner. And does thee have plans?"

The girl nodded gratefully but then, as though she had forgotten where she was, her gaze became fixed and troubled.

To introduce a light touch, Emily made the first comment that came into her head. "Thy frock is the loveliest color I believe I have ever seen. That rose silk positively glows."

The cloud on Mollie's face deepened. "I made a mistake when I purchased the goods."

"Why?" Emily protested, "Who is to say *thee* cannot wear what thee likes?"

Mollie moved uncomfortably. "The lieutenant said it is too bright. He likes me in blue."

"But....," began Emily.

"No, it's all right," Mollie declared hastily. "It's a small matter. I like to please him."

Emily said lightly, smiling, "I expect he is a very pleasant young man, but do not give up thine own preferences too easily."

Mrs. Dana had settled by Emily in time to hear her last remark. She now added, "That's right, Mollie. You're a most eligible young woman, handsome, talented and wealthy, though I suppose it is unseemly to mention that. There is no reason whatever to be humble in how you expect your young man to regard you."

Mollie shook her head with an uncertain smile which included both of them. Then the double doors opened and she anxiously watched for the lieutenant, as the gentlemen came through. After that, she had no attention to spare either of them.

Emily and Mrs. Dana exchanged only a long somber look before turning to the other gentlemen. At the end of the evening, however, in the privacy of Mrs. Dana's bedroom, as Emily tied her bonnet strings, that lady snapped, "Well, that's the shortest period of service I've ever heard of, over before it began!"

"Oh, don't be angry with her," pleaded Emily. "Poor girl, she's losing so much more than we are. And I'm afraid she half knows it already."

"Well, the little idiot, if she *knows,* why is she doing this?" And after a troubled pause, Mrs. Dana demanded, "How can such an exceptional woman as Mollie pick such a high and mighty jackanapes as that one?"

Emily, for once, had no answer.

Now, as the months ran on toward the end of Emily's first year at the camp, she took a few weeks to travel home to Sherwood, to catch her breath and regain strength. She left a substitute to dole out the shipments of needful clothes and foodstuffs which she had begged from friends.

On one of her first days at home, four-year-old Isabel came to stay with her Aunt Emily. "Let's see. What would thee like? Shall we see if there are any late hollyhocks and make hollyhock dollies and have a tea party with acorn cups and saucers? Thy mama and I sometimes did that."

As they went down the path together, Isabel turned aside to reach toward a web, spangled with dewdrops in the morning sunlight. "Don't break it, Belle," exclaimed Emily, catching her hand. "That's the spider's house."

Isabel stopped and looked closely at the web before asking, "How does she know how to make her house?"

"Why, Isabel, how does thy kitty know how to wash her face?" And as the child lifted bright eyes to hers, she added, "How does thy heart know how to beat?"

Isabel said no more of this while they busied themselves turning out several little ruffle-skirted ladies with oriental eyes. She must have thought it over during the day, however, for when she took up her mug at supper, she hesitated, and then set it back down. "Perhaps I should not drink my milk."

"Whyever not, Belle?" asked Emily, brushing back a lock of fair hair, just for the pleasure of touching the appealing child.

"I'm afraid I'll get my heart wet."

Since Mrs. Seward was planning to be back in Auburn soon, Emily saved up this anecdote and told it when she called there. She added, "I must admit I find the child irresistible. She is such a little companion. It is hard to be firm with her, but I do not believe she could be spoiled."

"One's children are a delight." Mrs. Seward smiled tenderly. "I remember how I would not let my little boys have their Christmas stockings one year until each of them counted his age in French."

"Thee brought them up with love and approval, and that's how Hannah treats Isabel."

Mrs. Seward smiled, and then turning the conversation, remarked, "I have hoped that either in Washington or here in Auburn, I could arrange for you to meet Harriet Tubman. I sent her a note and I am now hoping she may be able to stop here to call today."

Emily echoed, "Harriet Tubman!"

"Why are you surprised? Have you forgotten how you discomfited Henry one night with your questions?"

Emily first laughed, "Did thee notice that?" and then marveled, "I never had any idea of *thee* knowing about their smuggling fugitives."

"In truth, I not only knew about it..." Mrs. Seward paused.

Emily's eyes opened wide; she leaned closer and lowered her voice. "Thee took part?" At Mrs. Seward's nod, she confided, "I thought of bringing a fugitive to thy house one night." And now at last Emily had the comfort of telling the old bitter story to someone who understood her frustration and praised her intentions.

In the midst of this, the maid announced Harriet Tubman. Emily liked Mrs. Seward's manner on greeting her. "I am glad to see you, my friend. And this is Emily Howland who has wanted to meet you." As the two women smiled at each other, Mrs. Seward added, "As you did earlier, Emily has been working in the Washington camp."

"Oh, I's heard about Emily Howland," interrupted Harriet warmly, her big rough hand swallowing up Emily's in a strong grip.

They had barely begun comparing their ideas on the needs of the freedmen in Washington, when Mrs. Seward suddenly pressed her hand to her face with an involuntary gasp of pain. They regretfully left the poor lady with face drawn and both hands clamped to her jaw, while her maid hurried to her with a dose of laudanum.

This dismayed Emily, for on her arrival, Mrs. Seward had assured her that she was better, that Washington was so damp, she never felt as well there as here at home.

As they stood on the steps outside the Seward's door, Emily looked at Harriet Tubman, liking her very much: plain in appearance with her sad face scarred from a vicious blow in her youth, common in speech, yet steady in her gaze, single-minded and kindhearted. Emily impulsively said, "May I offer thee a ride?"

"Where was you heading?"

"Back out South Street, past thy home, but if thee is going the other way, I will be glad to take thee first."

"Land, ma'am," chuckled Harriet, "You ain't thinking I mind a few steps downtown?"

Emily thought of the hundreds of miles of enemy swamp and woodland this woman had trodden with her passengers in the Underground Railroad. Suddenly, she said in a rush, "I can't tell thee how much I have envied thee in thy work. For so many years I could do nothing, while *thee*— why, look how many people owe their freedom and the safety of their children, likely their very lives, to thee!"

Harriet's dark face shone with pleasure but, ducking her head awkwardly, she mumbled, "Go 'long with you, ma'am."

In November, much refreshed by her time with family and friends, Emily set off for Virginia in first-rate spirits. She arrived back at camp, jolting along with Uncle Moses in the market wagon, to a most gratifying reception by her beaming people who clustered about and nearly smothered her with their rejoicings. "We looked for you until we done give up!" one said. In the warmth of their welcome, she could almost ignore the mud and the heaps of at least ten thousand unburied rats.

Yes, this was where she belonged. They needed her...and for them, she could make a difference!

Coronilla: "Progress"

1864

Snow in Virginia! And even more exciting at this Christmastime was the camp's uprooting from the mud, in a move across the river to Arlington, the confiscated estate of General Robert E. Lee. This new camp boasted fifty-two log houses, a chapel and, to her joy, a larger schoolhouse. Here the hateful Mr. Nichols was to oversee the freedmen in raising crops to earn their tiny wages and pay their exorbitant rents.

Emily lingered behind a few days but wrote,

> There is a great deal there to be done. I greatly desire to go, but I must wait. Nichols is very jealous of his power and harasses and torments and thwarts all he can, but [the] way may open.

Emily had hated to appeal to Captain Ferree, but after all, Nichols could hardly detest her more. Thus by New Year's Day 1864, Emily had settled in at Camp Todd on the Arlington estate, under much more comfortable conditions than before. Even though Nichols would issue her no food rations, she and another woman were teaching about sixty children during the day and a varying number of adults in the evening.

The first time one elderly man came to the evening class, he quavered, "Is you sure we's safe here?"

Surprised, Emily asked, "Safe from what, uncle?"

"The night patrol!" He peered about fearfully, and at his words, several others also looked nervously over their shoulders.

"The night patrol? Is it true then that your masters sent spies to see if you had books?"

"Yes, miss," and others nodded.

"What happened if they caught someone trying to learn to read?"

"Most killed that black man!"

Grandfather was right, Emily realized anew. Knowledge *is* power. Withholding education from these people had been the only way to hold them in submission.

Ella, of course, was nearly always in the night class and, like many of them, was very quick and attentive. Seeing her age on the school record, Emily had said, "Thee must have married young."

"Wasn't but fifteen," Ella had agreed cheerfully. "But Lewis, he said even if he was too old, I'd be safer with him, when that old white boss was fixing to shine around. Lewis said he guessed I wouldn't have no trouble if I was married to him. And I didn't." She had sounded both proud and affectionate. Despite their ages, Emily had seen that it was a sound marriage between two bright and ambitious people. And again she had thought, "This girl needs no pity."

Nor would the rest of these freed people, if they could master the numbers and letters that were their passports to fair treatment.

Emily had heard, of course, that the president favored placing all Negroes in colonies elsewhere. Four million people? A physical impossibility! As Frederick Douglass said, "All the gold in California could never finance such a project." Besides, weren't most of them native Americans as much as Lincoln himself? She could not understand this one quirk of his, and if schooling could help them to resist, she and others like her would redouble their efforts.

Even so, one of the pleasures of her visits to the Seward home was that it faced directly across Lafayette Square toward the north portico of the White House, and she sometimes saw, pacing on the grounds, the tall, gangling president. She had learned to love him for his goodness of heart, however vehemently she disliked his colonization nonsense. Once, she caught a glimpse of him bending to talk with his son, Tad. How much she liked him for that open show of affection. And once, when the Union losses were disastrous, when each of his generals had turned out to be more do-less and inept than the last, and he was the target of jeers and hatred in the press, she had seen him pacing somberly alone. Though she had felt a surge of pity for him, she had admired his integrity when she read:

> *I desire so to conduct the affairs of this administration that if at the end, when I come to lay down the reins of power, I have lost every other friend on earth, I shall at least have one friend left, and that friend shall be down inside of me.*
>
> A. Lincoln.

Whether or not she saw the president, however, it was heartwarming to visit Mrs. Seward. Though the poor lady was now often ill with neuralgia and her abscessed teeth, and speaking longingly of going home to Auburn to stay, she and Fanny were always warmly welcoming to Emily.

On one of these visits, while Mrs. Seward was resting, Fanny and Emily settled in for a cozy chat.

"Thy poor mother! I am so sorry for all her suffering," said Emily sadly.

"I know," sighed Fanny, but added slowly, "I almost think having to live in Washington is harder for her than all the pain she bears." And, at Emily's enquiring look, she explained, "Mother hates public life, and all the pomp and show. The last time she had to attend a state dinner, she was right down in bed for two days."

Emily nodded. "I wonder if that is due to her upbringing. She told me once about her Quaker grandmother keeping house for her father and bringing up the girls. I've always felt that Quaker influence made a bond of tastes and interests between us."

Fanny agreed. "It certainly has made this artificial life uncongenial to her. She and Father are so fond of each other, but he wants her here with him where his life is, while her one desire is that he should retire quietly to Auburn with her."

"I didn't realize that. How hard it must be if neither can live the other's kind of life comfortably."

"During his years in Albany, they lived apart a good deal, and still do, yet they are never happy without each other." Here Fanny brushed her hand over her eyes.

Emily mulled this over and finally said, "I know thy mother is retiring. I wonder, though, if her summaries of those voluminous reports give her an influence, through thy father, on the political life of Washington greater than if she were the grandest hostess on the social scene. Certainly it is a more valuable influence."

Seeing the grateful tears in Fanny's eyes, Emily added, "I've always been so thankful to her for opening her home to me."

It was at the home of her friends, Dr. and Mrs. Breed, however, that Emily first met Cornelia Hancock, the nurse who had arrived during her weeks at home. Emily was delighted with the open, eager, sparkling creature who demanded, "Where are these good abolitionists in the North who talk so much and do so little? Why are they not down here working with these wretched Negroes they clamored for thirty years to have freed?"

Mollie, now a bride, was in the party looking wistfully from one face to the other as Cornelia and Emily exchanged stories about the oddities and absurdities of their days, to the amusement of the party. Even the surgeon, Dr. Breed, who spent his days amid the most dreadful of the Negro war casualties, chuckled. He did say, however, "These girls are heroines, you know."

Ignoring this, Cornelia said quickly, "Senator Sumner says a Freedmen's Bureau is being set up. We certainly need humane men who see these people as human beings, capable of improving themselves. You military men," she said saucily to Captain Ferree and another officer, "are more interested in your riding horses than in these poor souls you are supposed to regulate!" She smiled unaffectedly around the circle as almost everyone, including the officers, laughed.

Mollie was wearing a blue dress, Emily had noticed. She watched her husband with an anxious, hopeful smile which faded when his stiffness made it clear he thought Cornelia regrettably pert. And even Mollie's conformity gained her only a scowl. There was no pleasing him!

Echoing Emily's thought, later in the evening Cornelia muttered, "That poor girl acts like a dog waiting to see if she'll get a pat or a kick. What's the matter with her?"

"Thee doesn't know the worst of it, for thee never knew Mollie when she was herself," answered Emily. "She wore the most glowing colors and she was so high-spirited and laughing and delightful, I felt she could do anything she put her mind to!"

"Surely thee is not talking of this wan and wilted creature I saw tonight?" inquired Cornelia, facetiously.

"She was all that and more," confirmed Guilemia Breed. "And can you credit this, Lieutenant Martin told my husband he only married her because *she* wanted it." Crossly, she added, "He gained her fortune; she is his unpaid housekeeper and maid, and he dares to make it all out to be a favor he's done her. Oh, he is a hateful man!"

Cornelia mused, "This is not the first time that I've thought nature plays a trick on young women, paralyzing their wits when they size up prospective husbands. And the disease has to run its course. There is no prevention and no cure."

Emily answered, sadly, "I think Mollie is cured, but it came too late. And the pity is that she had so much she was planning to do, and now she is wasting herself in waiting on him. Poor Mollie!"

Poor Emily, she was more inclined to think when, several weeks later, she was making her way down the road at the Freedmen's Camp at Arlington with the mud sucking at her heavy shoes. She had expected they would leave the wallow behind when they moved across the river, but hundreds of feet soon scuffed any grass away and sank any boards laid across the muddy places.

Probably her home folks were crunching over clean, sparkling snow. Yet, after all, she would far rather be here, with the raw wind cutting through her cloak and whipping her bonnet ribbons across her face, than wasting her life there.

To her surprise, she suddenly met Cornelia Hancock, who cried cheerily, "Was it for this that I vowed to stay single?"

"Oh!" Emily stopped short. "Did thee also make such a vow?"

"I did, yes," admitted Cornelia, more soberly, "and I mean to stick to it. For here we have these wretched freedmen who need a white person to so much as get a coffin for their dead, or even to get them a pass. They wander around in the most forlorn manner. We can settle these matters for them, but how much could we do with babies clinging to our skirts and husbands waiting for their dinners?"

Emily agreed, but asked, puzzled, "What has happened to thy nursing duties?"

"The need at the hospital has worn itself out for now. I'm waiting for a summons to one of the Army hospitals near the fighting. In the meantime, I've come over here to be useful to thy freedmen."

"Good," said Emily, with much satisfaction, and the new friends sloshed on together.

It did cross her mind how odd the two of them must look. In this era of hoops and crinolines, with their sodden skirts plastered about their lean forms, they were specters from fifty years ago. Today, however, she didn't mind at all what sort of strange figures they were cutting, with Cornelia beside her to give her heart.

"I know now what it is," exclaimed Cornelia, suddenly. "I've been trying to think why I'd know these barracks are full of freedmen and not soldiers. It's because soldiers always have their washing out flapping on lines."

Emily was quick to defend her friends. "They do laundry like anybody when they have a change of clothes."

Cornelia assured her, "I didn't mean they are shiftless. I've seen them at work."

"Mr. Nichols calls them lazy, but they aren't," Emily declared. "They want to work. There are plenty of women here with husbands gone to war, who are desperate for work to feed their young ones. They'll launder; they'll pick rocks in the fields; they'll do anything respectable." Heaving a sigh, she confided, "I keep hoping the government will give each family a little farm. It would be the making of them."

Soon Emily was tilting her ear to catch the stirring strains sung by a company of soldiers marching smartly to drill, near the fort on the west ridge. "I love that song," she exclaimed, "that 'Battle Hymn' of Julia Ward Howe's," and she sang along with the men, "As He died to make men holy, let us die to make men free." To her companion, she said, "That's so fine, it makes shivers go up my spine."

Cornelia made an unexpectedly somber reply. "It should rather strike a chill to the marrow of thy bones. Thee doesn't know what that song means until thee has seen fine young men maimed and wasted on a battlefield as I saw them at Gettysburg. Thee may take my word, death was the better end for them."

Emily looked at her in startled dismay.

"Oh, I know," Cornelia went on bitterly. "I've seen the recruitment parades with the bands playing and the flags waving and people cheering for the boys who sign up. I've seen excited girls begging for buttons off their uniforms as they leave, to make into earrings! But in the twenty-one hospitals in a ring around this city, our battle heroes are rotting. Surely thee has seen the coffins for sale along the streets and embalmers vying for the custom of grief-stricken parents, come to take their boys home?"

Emily was speechless with dismay as Cornelia pointed after the marching company. "Those young men right there, men with their lives before them, fathers of young families—many of them are going to be broken and killed. What kind of a nation are we?"

Emily faltered, "I...I had hardly thought...."

Cornelia, though her pretty face was sad, patted Emily's arm. "We aren't supposed to think. We could not carry on a war if people started to think." And more calmly, she added, "I feel better for saying it, though."

They trudged on, each deep in thought, until Emily exclaimed, "Oh, since thee is right here, I wish thee would step in and see one of my old uncles."

Cornelia, after inspecting the ulcer on his leg and hearing what Emily had done for it, nodded. "Thee did just right." As they left she added, "It surprises me that thee is not a nurse. Thee has an aptitude."

Emily cried, "But in the time I could heal a few, I can teach fifty. And they can teach others." She stopped abruptly. It was not very courteous to say to Cornelia, "What I teach them makes them far more able, all their lives long, than merely healing their wounds." No, she could not say that to Cornelia.

For the first time, however, she saw that teaching satisfied all of her dreams. She thought back once more with the deepest gratitude to Frances Seward for her encouragement, and for her three words: born to teach!

A few days later, Emily's mail included a letter from home announcing Ben's appointment as cashier at the new bank in Union Springs. Well, good for Ben!

She hoped this might please his wife; she was so ambitious. While Emily was home, she had clearly seen Louise's discontent at Ben's working in the office of Father's Auburn mill. Emily had noticed several times how anxious he looked whenever Louise was by.

If she approved of his new position, Emily supposed she would be rewarding Ben with her smiles now. Refolding the sheets, Emily sighed. Poor Ben! Suddenly, she noticed another letter in her pile of mail. Why, this was from Cornelia. Wherever had she got to in the last few days?

3rd Division, 2nd Corps Hosp.
Brandy Station, Virginia

Feb. 10, 1864

Dear Friend,

I was sorry to leave without a word of farewell to thee, but the call here was sudden and urgent.

I find myself comparing my arrival at this place to Gettysburg. There I found the wounded lying about on boards and covered with straw, with no one to give them a morsel even though there were wagons loaded with bread and provisions. I laugh to recall how I sat on the ground, breaking off pieces of bread and spreading jelly with a stick, to carry to the men on a shingle.

This hospital is quite the opposite, well arranged and very clean. Dr. Dudley, the major surgeon in charge here, would not tolerate anything less, although surprisingly, he is only about my own age, I would guess perhaps twenty-three.

Gettysburg comes back to my mind because when Dr. Dudley and I met, we both exclaimed, "Ah, we have met before!" He was one of the wounded to whom I had carried food on the battlefield there.

He is a most unusual doctor for he will listen to a woman's ideas; he allows me to do as I think best and has put me in charge of the cooks and the meals, as well as overseeing the care of the wounded.

Thee would not approve of the doctor's views of your freedmen, for he does not see them as people. I intensely dislike his teasing of the bright black boy who serves him. Just so would he tease a clever dog and put it through its tricks, though he would do anything to help a suffering colored man.

He is a graduate of Yale, yet the men of his regiment regard him highly, for he never sets himself above them.

As a surgeon he is quick and skillful and we work well as a team.

I would never say all this to my mother, but she need not be alarmed, for thee knows how we vowed to remain unwed. And I have always found myself to be immune to the tender emotions.

From thy friend,

Cornelia Hancock.

Emily looked at the last sentences, shaking her head as she tried to reconcile them with the warmhearted young woman she knew.

At least, she thought with a sigh, Cornelia was working with a colleague whose aims matched her own, unlike Emily. The hateful Mr. Nichols was now refusing to let her people plant gardens for their own use on the land they were renting, though she was personally furnishing the seeds and a hoe apiece. "They need the fresh vegetables desperately," she argued.

"It would cut their time in the field," he was insisting, obstinately.

Much as she regretted aggravating Nichols, she again went over his authority to Captain Ferree for permission for the little gardens. Her people immediately began scratching away with their hoes far into the evening, proving they needed no prodding when they had a chance to work for themselves.

Emily had wondered how Ella's husband, a big able man who was only in his mid-forties, had escaped being pressed into the army. She met him on her rounds one day, and stopped to inquire for Ella.

Lewis Carter shook his head. "Well, she's not so bad off as the ones with their men gone to war."

Afterward, Emily would wonder how she had ever come to ask such a personal question. At that moment, knowing they both loved Ella, it felt natural to ask Lewis how he had managed to stay out of the Army.

"I wasn't about to leave, with that Nichols anywhere near my woman. So he said he'd keep me to help oversee the field work if I'd work like four men. He sure 'nough sees to it I do. Treats me like a pack mule, he does." Glancing about, he added, "I best get along, 'fore he sees me standing."

Looking in his kind, tired face, as he turned to go, Emily said, "I believe thee was wise."

The unfairness of Nichols now fell even more heavily upon the women, including poor Ella, for as soon as they had learned to count and demand their rightful pay, he cut their hours of work.

Emily, coming back from her rounds one evening, stopped by their shack. Ella, looking downcast, was watching her husband hoeing vigorously in their garden, even after his long day of field work. What a worker this man was, to be sure!

It was Ella who answered her enquiry. "We thought it would be different here." With a wry smile, she added, "It's getting to be more 'O Lord' than 'Thank God.'"

Lewis lifted his head from his hoeing. "They'd ought to give us a piece of old master's land. We worked enough years to earn it."

"I think so, too," agreed Emily.

"Do you think they will?"

"I can't say, but I do hope so," she answered soberly. Then, suddenly noticing Ella's figure in profile, she exclaimed in surprise, "Why, Ella!"

Ella hunched her shoulders. "I don't want another baby born here. What chance has any young'un got in a place like this? We can't hardly feed the two we got."

However, Emily did see her in their garden, another day, hoeing with vigor. "That Nichols, he can't stop me working in my own garden," the girl said, defiantly.

When Emily reported to Captain Ferree about the success of the little garden plots, he asked, "What about you? Are you getting enough to eat?"

"I must admit, I can get no rations from Mr. Nichols, but I still have cheese and dried beef I brought from home, and as long as I am able to buy buckwheat flour for pancakes and beans to bake for supper, I do very well."

Naturally, he wanted to force Nichols to issue rations to her, but this she firmly refused to permit. In fact, she spoke so vehemently, she was certain he would not again try to gain any personal favors for her.

To her deep dismay, almost immediately she found herself writing:

> *Camp Todd, Va*
> *March 22, 1864*
>
> *Dear Mrs. Seward*
>
> *Capt. Ferree told me that he has asked you to use your influence to obtain a horse for my use. This intended kindness on his part annoys me so much that I feel like writing to you at once to unsay whatever he has said, and to beg you not to think of it. He is one of those persons of generous impulsiveness with whom to think is to speak whether it is fit or not. And having heard me once say that I wished I might have a horse detailed to ride my circuit, he dashes off with the idea, ready to perpetrate any absurdity in its behalf.*
>
> *I do not wish the friendship which I have always felt a privilege and an honor to possess, desecrated by being made the vehicle for asking favors. I have done too much of it already.*
>
> *407 are to arrive at Arlington today from one of the abortive attempts of gov't at colonization.*
>
> *I never could understand how a mind that could put two and two together, could seriously consider the matter.*
>
> *This side of Father Abraham's character always disgusted me. It seemed silly.*
>
> *I must close and ring the school bell.*
>
> *Yours lovingly, gratefully,*
>
> *Emily Howland.*

Even more did she feel the imposition of the captain's request when she learned that Mrs. Seward was now so ill she had gone home to Auburn to stay.

Thus Emily's next act was to make it exceedingly clear to the chagrined Captain Ferree that she would only accept help for her people. That done, and ignoring his wounded look, she could get back to normal. And when she next received a letter from Cornelia, she felt that even with short rations and no horse, she was fortunate indeed in comparison:

Field Hospital near Richmond
June l0th 1864

Dear Friend,

How thee would envy me if thee could see me, idling on the back piazza of a grand old mansion here behind the lines, writing letters like a leisured lady.

I could almost forget the war for these few moments, except that an embalmed Lieutenant is keeping me company on the piazza; also an occasional shell explodes nearby but we are all accustomed, and pay no heed.

Dr. Dudley is a very satisfactory dr., except that he seems bent upon getting shot again. A bullet struck him in the shoulder at Gettysburg because he was out attending the wounded on the battle front. Here he has even less excuse, for he goes right up the breast works out of sheer curiosity. The two lines are only a few yards apart and I ask him, if he gets shot through the head, what will this hospital do then?

I think of thee and trust that the mud at Arlington has dried up and the little gardens are flourishing.

I find myself thriving on this life; I used to often be sickly, but I am never ill a day here. Events always work to the good for me.

from thy friend, Cornelia H.

Emily's suspicions about Dr. Dudley's growing importance to their friend were echoed by Mrs. Breed, who shared her letters from Cornelia. He had now joined his regiment but still rode to the hospital to call on Cornelia twice a week, and wrote often as well.

"Oh dear, how troublesome these men are," exclaimed Emily in tones all the more heartfelt because, as she had feared, every kindness Captain Ferree had done for her had further inflamed his ardor. At last, she headed off a proposal only by explaining to him that, for herself, she held a negative view of marriage and advised him, if he were thinking of it, to enter that state only after great deliberation and caution.

Tactful though she had tried to be, the doglike devotion and hurt in his eyes now caused her such discomfort that she was almost glad to hear that he was assigned elsewhere.

One of General Early's raiding parties had slipped inside the Freedmen's Village in July, revealing the woeful inadequacy of the Yankee fortifications. Luckily, the sixty armed Rebels had made so much noise, the freedmen heard their approach when a mile off and blew their horns, alerting the troops in time to drive off the raiders. Even so, Emily had a taste of what Cornelia was living with daily: an enemy close enough to shoot.

Emily did make a visit at home after this episode, but upon returning to camp in the fall, she calmly wrote of "her flock":

Washington
Nov. 30 1864

> *They were overjoyed to see me. They attribute all their misfortunes to my leaving them, now I suppose they anticipate a dawn of prosperity.*
>
> *One day I walked over to Camp Rucker to see the school under my supervision there. In the p.m. a friend loaned me her horse and I rode over to Hall's Mill where they are very anxious to have a school. I staid [sic] in her neat little cabin all night, taught some of my old pupils there.*
>
> *I am now such a veteran in the service that I everywhere find my people.*

However, to Major General Dana, at whose home she had stayed in Washington as she returned, she had betrayed more anxiety:

"Morale is bad and will be worse, as long as that spiteful cheating Nichols supervises the camp." And she repeated Uncle Moses' ominous words about Nichols, which had haunted her.

"Humph! Did he say that? Isn't Moses Washington that impressive, white-haired giant of a driver? Well, I'd say he's probably a sound judge."

"But what can anyone do against this great clanking machine of government?"

To her surprise, he had answered cryptically, "Sometimes a flea in the right ear is enough."

Only time would tell what that might amount to.

To Emily's pleasure, she had hardly unpacked on her return when a letter came from Cornelia:

City Point, Va.
Nov. 1864
My dear friend:

> *I was dismayed to hear in September from Guilemia Breed that thee was leaving Washington.*
>
> *Now I hear thee is back on duty with thy freedmen.*
>
> *I was sure thee could not be satisfied away from thy work. Nor can I, tho' when we retreated this summer, I ate*

hardtack on the march along with the soldiers. We were even caught in shellfire once. We had several pretty hard days but thee knows I have always said good fortune follows me.

As I feared, tho', Dr. Dudley persisted in tending the wounded in the front lines, and was captured by the Rebels. I do not know if he is living. He well knew the risk he took, for he had sent his horses to the rear and had given his new gold watch to one of the other doctors. I've heard no word from him since. This is so unlike him that I would fear for his life, except that I cannot believe him dead. However, I should be quieter in mind if I could only know.

It is very fortunate that I am busy every hour of the day. Among my duties, I am in charge of the kitchen, of course, feeding about 300 men. All this fills my mind and keeps me as content as may be.

If any of thy circle of friends intend doing anything for the needful, I expect they will give to thy wretched freedmen. I am begging for my soldiers, of course. I should be happy to have a letter from thee telling of thy work.

from thy friend Cornelia H.

Several busy weeks later, Emily replied to Cornelia's request for a letter.

Camp Todd.
Jan. 6 1865

Dear Cornelia,

In my cabin, very comfortable except for the smoke. Have been teaching all day, have 43 scholars, very eager and interested. The skyline here is all prickly with circling forts and army tents now, and all the fortifications which were seen as necessary when those Rebs crept in. I now feel as though I, like thee, am living just behind the battle lines. I went this evening to see my Uncle Moses who has been poorly. I drew him out about his old slave life. Uncle Moses is one of those who has lived so near the Light Within that it has illumined his hard life all along.

He endured working for the same brutal master for 16 years; he ran away, chased by dogs and armed men but escaped, though he was later recaptured.

He had a chance to go north on a boat but did not trust the looks of the captain. Afterward he learned the man would have held him for a reward from his master.

Well, dear friend, our conditions are well enough here. I begin to suspect, tho', that our government has never had the slightest intention of granting plots of land from the confiscated southern plantations to these Negro families. I shall not despair yet.

Thy friend, Emily

Despite this gnawing suspicion, every prospect looked bright when she learned that they had seen the last of Superintendent Nichols. Her elation lasted only until she made her circuit of calls to see how her flock was faring. Then she discovered one of the households frantically bundling their possessions for instant flight.

"Oh Lordy, Miss Emily, that new Captain Brown, he's a'going to steal away our young ones!" And to her consternation, Emily learned it was true: soldiers were on their way to seize, at bayonet point, all children over twelve to be bound out as indentured servants.

By a happy chance, the captain's order had leaked out through a kindly neighboring farmer. It was only due to his benevolent interest in the little colony that, when the soldiers came dashing up for the children, there were none. Several of these families had fled just outside the camp, where they were throwing together flimsy shacks. Though outside the government's jurisdiction, they were still close enough so Emily could reach them in her round of calls.

Emily, aflame over this new outrage, dropped in to talk it over with Ella, and perhaps also to renew her acquaintance with the girl's children, including little Lewis, who had been a newborn when Emily came back from Sherwood in November.

When they walked to the door after their visit, Ella was holding her baby, and Emily paused to take one little hand and smile down into his dark liquid eyes.

Suddenly, Ella's face crumpled and she exclaimed passionately, "I wants prospects to get better for my young'uns, but they's getting worse."

And all Emily could say was, "I know."

One evening soon after, opening the door to a knock, she beheld Uncle Moses Washington, shifting his hat nervously in his huge hands.

"Why, Uncle," she smiled, seeing that he was wearing his Sunday clothes. "Is thee honoring me with a call of state?"

"I wants to talk to you about a great worry to me," he answered with dignity.

Immediately sobering, she drew out a chair for him and sat down facing him, attentively.

"You's so good, but I never heard you say you's baptized of the water and the Spirit."

Emily smiled warmly at this good friend. "Thee must make thy faith broad enough to take me in without baptism."

He shook his head, his wise old eyes mournful. "I wants to meet you up there. I don't want you to be lost."

When he finally left, she saw that he would like to urge her more, but he said only, "You won't mind if I prays for you, Miss Emily?"

She sat on, thinking of him, the dear man, and her thoughts drifted to Ella and some of the others, and it came to her, *"I love these people!"*

On March 4th, 1864, the day of Lincoln's second inauguration, Emily rode in the market wagon with Uncle Moses, through sloppy spring mud and across the bridge to the city to see the procession. She could not get close enough to the Capitol Building to hear the president speak, though she could see the platform built on the east steps. Still it was very moving to be in the mass of people stretching as far as her eye could see, and to be a part of the roar that went up as Lincoln stepped to the platform.

Straining her eyes to see his figure in the distance, she wondered what he was thinking. He had never expected re-election, after the punishment he had taken from the press during these four bloody years. Now the tide of the war had turned and so had the public's feeling toward him. Was he elated today?

As silence fell over the vast crowd, the sun suddenly broke through the clouds, streaming down on the man who was speaking. All about her, Emily heard quick indrawn breaths of wonder.

Afterward, knowing Fanny Seward would have been standing with the wives of the Cabinet members on the Capitol steps, behind and above the platform, Emily paid her a call at home. First, she inquired for Mrs. Seward, saying, "I'm glad she is back in Auburn, but I miss her so much," to which Fanny agreed, with a deep sigh.

Then, "What did the president say?" Emily asked eagerly.

"His concern is all for the healing of the rift between North and South. I recall his words, 'with malice toward none, with charity for all.'"

"I might have known," Emily exclaimed. "He hasn't a petty or conceited bone in his body, has he? It is just not in him to rejoice over a personal victory when the war has cost our country so dearly."

Jouncing along back to camp beside Uncle Moses, she told him all about it, the president's modest attitude despite the resounding cheers of the crowd, and the words Fanny remembered, "With malice toward none, with charity for all."

"That Uncle Sam!" Uncle Moses shook his white head in wondering admiration. "He's got a great heart!"

When her people gathered that night to hear about it, she told them it was the grandest day in this country's history. They cheered when she told them how the sun broke through the clouds as Lincoln stood forth to speak, as if blessing him.

"Bless that Uncle Sam!" called out several of them.

By the next Sunday, a friend had copied the Inaugural address for her to read to her families. Again they cheered when they heard how Lincoln had said it was "strange that men ask God's assistance to wring bread from the sweat of other men's brows."

At first she thought it was a spring of good omens. For the first time, she was a guest at tea in the home of a white neighbor, who then entered her two boys in Emily's colored school. When asked how he liked it, one of the boys answered, "I don't know. What's different about it?"

And in early April, the Union took Richmond and the war was virtually over. Bells rang and guns of victory boomed from every fort, rocking the earth beneath the feet of Emily and her laughing, cheering, dancing freedmen.

Within the very week of this jubilation came horrifying news: the president was dead, by an assassin's bullet. The disaster stunned her colored friends. The skies wept and the air was thick with gloom, to Emily's grieving mind.

Her people clustered around, and Ella spoke for all when she cried out, "O Lord, O Lord, what will become of us all now?"

Every cabin wore its little black badge of mourning: an old lace veil, a piece of fringe or a strip of cotton.

Well, life must go on, so Susy, one of Emily's helpers, went for the milk. She came flying back with the fearful news that a would-be assassin had also stabbed Secretary of State Seward in his bed. If Seward had not been wearing a thick leather and steel neck brace following a carriage accident a few days earlier, the knife would have found its fatal mark.

One old auntie came to see Miss Emily that evening, saying, "When I heard 'Uncle Sam' was dead, I cried, 'O Jesus, why did you let this be done?'"

Emily recalled the news item she had read only two days before: President Lincoln, while speaking to a crowd outside the White

House after Lee's surrender, asked them, "What shall we do with the Confederates?" A voice from the crowd called out, "Hang them!" Tad, as close to his father as usual, had shouted, "No, no, papa, not *hang* them! Hang *on* to them!" and Mr. Lincoln with a wide smile had called to the crowd, "Tad has got it. We must hang *on* to them!"

Now who was there to continue "hanging on to the Confederates," while trying "with malice toward none" to "bind up the nation's wounds"?

Emily wrote of the only comfort she could find in all this:

Lincoln's star had culminated, he had finished his great work, the whole nation revered him, the four million freedmen nearly worshipped him. This was the glorious time for him to die. At no time in his later life could his memory be so precious.

She was also very distressed over Mrs. Seward, whom she could not get out of her mind. That dear woman, already so ill and frail, had rushed back to Washington to be with her poor battered "Henry" after his carriage accident. What terror she must have felt when that madman pushed into her home, intent on killing her husband or anyone else who got in his way. Would that gentle lady's nervous system ever recover from such a hideous shock?

Deepest of all was Emily's distress for her poor colored friends. What would become of them now?

Mallow: "Sweetness"

1865

Emily had rejoiced when the new Freedmen's Bureau opened, just before Lincoln's death. Sympathetic experts would now improve the wretched conditions of her people, she told herself during her busy summer of teaching and administration at the Arlington camp.

In my cabin
June 8, 1865

Dear Mother:

The milk I get at night is often sour in the morning and I have learned to like clabber.

I sometimes treat some of the poor old aunties to a taste and I think with regret of the pans of it given to the swine at home.

I find dear Aunt Mary's remedy "Crane's Bill" invaluable. It grows abundantly all about here. I have cured Uncle Henry & Aunt Mary and the fame is gone all abroad. My diet is mostly bread and cheese and tea.

If you send a package, I would like one of my drawing books, for I have taken to making sketches.

Mr. Johnson, teacher at Camp Rucker, is very anxious that I should go and help him organize. Is it not strange how much more a small woman can do than a large man. I used to have a prejudice in favor of large people or their ability, it is all gone now. They look the best, that is all.

Farewell. I am glad Belle is such a nice little girl, but she has had remarkable training.

In my cabin
6 mo. 20, 1865

Dear father:

   Thine of the 17th containing the very welcome draft
came to hand this p.m. I was just about write again, for I
was moneyless. I do not like to get out of the needful. I am
inclined to excessive economy and I have ample chance to
practice it. Hard work and very poor fare do not go well
together.

By fall, her high hopes for the new Freedmen's Bureau were fading.

As Ella pointed out one day, "Our men works harder than ever, but we gets poorer and poorer." The girl had come to Emily shamefacedly, with the rags of her old, thin skirt gathered about her. "I caught it on a nail," she explained and went on bitterly, "We wants to keep ourselves. If they would just let us work and pay us fair, I could buy myself a skirt."

Emily fished in the Aid Society barrel but could find only a dark, heavy skirt.

Ella put it on, but the flare of her nostrils gave away how she detested it. Trying to smile, she said, "Sure 'nough, it's 'O Lord' now." The droop of her thin shoulders as she went down the steps told Emily that she referred to far more than the ugly skirt.

When Emily went home to Sherwood for the winter, she was already sputtering to her father, "Anything the government undertakes costs more and is worse done. This 'wise' bureau's first act is to cancel the food rations for the teachers. Don't they know that schooling is the only way to get the Negroes on their feet?"

"Will the loss of rations make such a difference?"

"Oh, yes, Father! Most of the teachers have barely eked out a living even with rations furnished." Indignantly, she continued, "And now the Bureau says colored women can't work in the fields. Thee cannot imagine the want and misery this Bureau is spreading."

As she painted her father's portrait that winter in Sherwood, she shared her frustration for her people: "They do not forget their unpaid years as slaves. They've said over and over to me, 'We's earned a piece of Old Boss's land.' Why didn't the government take off little homesteads for them? Their masters, who lived at ease from their bitter toil, would hardly miss those bits of land. But no! There will never be fair treatment for anyone whose skin is black."

She paused, remembering how she and Uncle Moses, in the long silent line of mourners, had looked their last on "Uncle Sam" as he lay in his black-draped glass bier. Whites and blacks, elbow to elbow, had grieved together at losing their friend.

Now she asked, doubtfully, "Father, does thee think even Lincoln could have brought a fair and peaceful reconstruction to the South?"

The resulting discussion led up to a proposition Emily wanted Father to consider. She felt very hopeful, because she and her brothers often chuckled about Father's "slight madness" for buying properties as they became available. They said he spent half his time arranging for searches and transfers of title. And his purchases were not just in Sherwood; his interest in woolen mills ranged from Oswego to Toronto and Toledo. Would he consider her idea?

"Now Father," she began, "the way to elevate Negroes out of their rags and dependency is to let them earn their own land. And I think I see how we can do it."

Glad she was that her mother was not sitting by. How she would have sniffed and sighed at all this. Mother, however, was up and about less and less. Whatever her ailment, it had taken firm hold of her this winter.

"Father," Emily continued earnestly, "some former slaveholders are selling tracts of land off their plantations at such low prices as thee would scarcely credit."

He always listened patiently to her but she had riveted his attention now.

"Would thee consider backing my purchase of a block of land where I might take a few of my families? I believe we could make it pay." Emily painted industriously, scarcely daring to look at him while he mulled it over. She had thought of this so much, it was a hope as fragile as a dream.

But Slocum Howland almost never refused his daughter anything within reason, and just as rarely did he refuse a bargain in real estate. Consequently, Emily returned to Virginia in April, authorized to look for a few hundred acres at a low price.

"Uncle Moses, our dream is coming true," she exclaimed, when he came to the Danas' Washington home to fetch her back to Freedmen's Village.

The big, rugged man reached for her satchels with a broad smile. "So we's going to look for that Promised Land, Miss Emily?"

As they jolted back over the bridge to Arlington in the market wagon, they talked of their proposed move, what they would plant, how they would use oyster shells for lime, and how they could manage this first winter for shelter.

Upon reaching Washington, she had written in her journal:

> *Apr. 1866: Trip from Sherwood. What a transition from winter to summer, from entire seclusion to the gay Capitol [sic].*

Now this delightful interlude was behind her and another transition lay before her. Emily, newly assigned to live outside Fort Morton for security, looked about as they drew up before the vacant cabin. "This is mighty unhandy, it's so far from Freedmen's Village. And I wonder if I shall die of loneliness?"

"Now Miss Emily, you won't have no time for dying," Uncle Moses assured her. "They already wants you at Camp Rucker School where one of our black boys sassed a white soldier."

Even as Emily clucked, her mind leaped ahead, planning how she would tackle this threat.

This was far from the only argument Miss Emily was to smooth out. In the meantime, she reopened her school at Freedmen's Village and greeted her students. They were more eager than ever to master their letters and numbers, partly to avoid being cheated in their dealings.

Some had scattered about the countryside, so at each of the forts there was now a little Negro settlement with a small school. And because she dealt with any kind of problem, the Freedmen's Bureau had asked her to supervise the untrained teachers in these five schools, in addition to her own teaching. She received no pay for frequently jolting over thirteen miles of rocky track in a ramshackle cart, or for hiking over five more of even rougher terrain.

Yet one day as she tramped briskly on her round, she caught herself grinning at the recollection of Nurse Cornelia Hancock's declaration, "There I was at Gettysburg, dark as an Indian and dirty as a pig, and as well as ever I had been!" Yes, despite long days and hard work, Emily also was healthier and happier than she had ever been, now that she was "making a difference."

> *Fort Morton*
> *Apr 22, 1866*
>
> *The other day I went to the city to the great celebration the colored people made in memory of the day they were set free. I marched with the schools, 300 with their teachers. A man who looked at us said, "The abolitionists may go it. They won't go it long."*
>
> *On the avenue, there was a procession an hour long passing with beautiful banners and flags. Some were*

soldiers carrying torn flags from battle. A great crowd gathered in front of the President's house, and he made a speech and shook hands with a good many.

At Franklin Square 15,000 or more nearly filled the 6 acres. While one of the senators was talking, the platform broke and the senators & generals went down in a heap, but pretty soon the Senator had mounted another stand and was speaking again.

We all went away tired but glad for the day.

Although the freedmen had cast aside their cares for this one gala day, she still agonized over their predicament. Those in her camp could find no jobs, but they could garden vigorously to raise something to eat. Those outside were even worse off.

Horace Greeley was grumbling in his *Tribune*, "If we give the Negro a bayonet, why can we not give him a ballot?"

Emily was more inclined to ask, "Why can we not first grant him a little place of his own?"

When she first came back through Washington this spring, she had stopped to call on Fanny Seward, wanting to share her sympathy and her own grief over Mrs. Seward's death. Fanny, however, was staying with a friend, but William Seward appeared at his study door to speak to Emily.

She had hardly recognized the man, with his face so disfigured from his attacker's knife, and looking so old and ill and sad. Nevertheless, as the secretary of state, he wielded enormous influence, and she seized the chance to appeal to him.

"I am sick over the way I see our freedmen living," she had begun. "It was criminal to tear them from their African homes to be forced labor to enrich whites. Now they're torn from even that poor security and told they are free. How are they free when they are destitute? These people are good workers, yet I see them out wandering the roads, with no jobs and no homes. And if they are arrested for vagrancy, they can be put out as bonded servants. Can't thee do something?"

Throwing out his hands helplessly, Seward had started to explain that since Congress and President Johnson were already clashing....

She had cut in impatiently, "Oh, I know. Isn't there a more direct way, through some agency? If these people were anyone else, they'd be robbing and looting!" Pausing to look at his troubled face, she pleaded, "What they all want is a little bit of land. They don't ask much, just five or ten acres, they say. After all their years of unpaid toil, haven't they earned that much?"

As she left, it was only by pinching her lips together that she had held back the bitter taunt, "I never thought I would hear William H. Seward say, 'Yes, but....'"

Was this the William Seward who, ten years ago, sold property to Harriet Tubman on elegant South Street in Auburn? The same Seward who once coolly defended a demented Negro murderer while half of Auburn threatened him with bodily harm if he dared do so?

Thinking over this unsatisfactory meeting, she wrote in her camp journal:

Apr 13, 1866: Poor Seward. He seems in his dotage, or to have lost all good.

She did realize that President Johnson's compromising away the Negroes' rights was not of Secretary Seward's doing. Surely, though, if dear Mrs. Seward were still alive to stiffen his resolve, he would have stood stronger for them. At any rate, when they had parted that day, she was glad she had held back her cruel words, for the poor man said heavily that Fanny was far from well, and he begged Emily to call on her again.

On the bright side, Emily rejoiced in a letter from Cornelia, who had been let down and bored at the end of her war nursing.

Mt. Pleasant, South Carolina
Dear Emily,

Well, despite my friends at home predicting disasters for me because I am "too young & pretty" to set off alone (ha!) I arrived in perfect safety in this beautiful town across the harbor from Charleston.

Thee would have laughed to see my first class of black youngsters off the street, gathered about me on the steps of an unused church. But they came back the next day bringing others. There on those steps, sheltered by live oaks, my school grew day after day, until a sympathetic gentleman, Mr. Laing, offered us a large 2-story building.

I am not sure thee believed, when thee sent me the $75. for my fare & expenses, that I really could start a school in a town where I knew not a soul. But as I've told thee, events always work to the good for me.

From thy grateful & busy friend, Cornelia H.

As she folded the sheets, Emily puzzled over Cornelia's omitting any mention of Dr. Frederick Dudley. Right after the war she had written one bald announcement of his release from Libby Prison, and never another word about him. Well, whatever was in Cornelia's mind and heart, there was nothing so healing as being very busy.

For Emily, her only regret in being so very busy herself was that she had no time to hunt for her block of plantation land, so she had engaged an agent, Ephraim Nash, formerly of Auburn. He soon wrote that he had located two attractive properties in his area, far down the Potomac on the Northern Neck of Virginia, and he urged her to take the boat trip down to inspect them.

Northumberland, Virginia
June 9, 1866

Well Father, I am away down here using my eyes as wisely as I can. I spent yesterday riding around that tract of land of which E. Nash wrote thee. I have wished for thee to see the land & the production. I shall send in this a specimen of cotton raised by "Uncle Aleck" who lives near.

The cotton is raised, carded, spun, dyed & woven in their own hands. During the war, the Rebel ladies dressed in it, wore it to church, to show they could do without the Yankees.

The tract of land has some rich bottom, the property of a large landholder who has great need of money.

The man who owns this has a great deal of land, some near the river which would please me better, that is, my eye and my palate for oysters. That tract is 300 acres, has a house and water power, asks 10 dollars an acre. I should like the river tract best but either will answer my purpose. I like the country, the flowers and the mocking-birds, all but its remoteness. What does thee think of the place on the river? We had a dish last night for supper I had never tasted before. It had crabs. They were very good eating. We had oysters also. They are eaten here all summer and thought especially good.

First Day 10th June
On the steamboat Columbia *for Washington.*

E. Nash thinks the landowner would sell for $1600, he is so pushed for money. I may go down again in midsummer vacation & then finish the matter.

Emily

As she inspected the plantation land, Emily had thought several times of the joy she was about to give Ella. Accordingly, upon her return to camp, she called at the Carters' cabin. Catching sight of the girl at work in the garden with her big baby tied firmly on her hip, Emily stopped, unseen.

Ella was not beautiful now; her face was hollow-cheeked and grim. Even when she spied Emily, she did not smile. "Why'd they bring us here if they's goin' treat us like this? You know they's goin' cut off all rations the first of October? By then, garden stuff's all gone. We was better off with Old Boss than here! If we's to feed our young'uns, we's got to go somewhere else."

"Thee is going, Ella," said Emily quickly. "I'm buying a tract on the Northern Neck and I'm taking my three special families to start with."

When Ella could take it in, the tight muscles of her face relaxed in a torrent of tears and such a shaking of her whole body that her baby began to wail. When she could calm herself and soothe the little boy, she said with a watery chuckle, "Ain't I just a silly?"

Here Emily could not resist saying, "Ella, that boy is too heavy for thee to carry like that."

"It's the only way to keep track of this one." Then, with such a smile as Emily had not seen from Ella in many months, she added ruefully, "Less'n I drive a post and hitch him to it. And the other two are so good and easy."

Now Emily thought to caution, "Oh, but do not tell any other families of our plan, for everyone will want to go and I cannot right all the wrongs of this wretched Freedmen's Village."

The thin tired face was alight with hope now. "You means we's going to work for you?"

"No, I mean for you people to be working for yourselves, to buy your farms out of your earnings."

Seeing Ella's eyes filling again, Emily caressed little Lewie's head and hurried away to give the poor girl a chance to cry in private.

At Dana's, in the drawing room before dinner one evening, she was just explaining to her circle of friends that, rather than hand out seeds to a hundred families herself, she gave them through the colored preacher.

Major General Dana, always warmly interested in her doings, was just asking, "Why is that?" Then, as he glanced over her shoulder, he interrupted himself to exclaim, smiling, "Well, Charles! Another officer of hollow rank!" Turning, Emily saw him punching the arm of a uniformed newcomer, who retorted in a deep voice, "Well, look at you, with your two stars!" Then they both laughed.

While the stranger ran his eyes around the group, smiling and nodding to acquaintances, Emily sized him up: tall, with broad shoulders and strong features, yet with pleasant crinkles by his eyes, a man who somehow drew all eyes.

And then General Dana was saying, "Emily, this is Colonel Charles Folsom; Miss Emily Howland, who comes to us from New York State."

The colonel greeted Emily courteously and even added in his deep voice, "Are you enjoying your stay here?" Clearly, however, he was not much attending to her reply even before he turned back to General Dana with a question.

At dinner, Emily's eyes turned to his end of the table frequently, for though he was not speaking loudly, he was somehow the center of attention. And twice his indifferent glance ran absently over her and slid away, unseeing.

Well, why should she care, she scolded herself, jerking her eyes back to Mrs. Dana.

"You had not met Colonel Folsom before, Emily?" that lady now asked her.

"No," and, equalling his indifference, she murmured, "but he seems an agreeable person."

In the same low tone, Mrs. Dana said, "He's chief quartermaster for this district." Then, at Emily's blank look, she smiled. "I see that doesn't mean anything to you. Well, then, he was only fifteen when he graduated from Harvard with honors, so my husband tells me."

Yes, that was impressive, Emily thought. And how strange that she, who had suffered far more interest than she wanted from several admirers, should now feel piqued simply because one attractive man had no eyes for her. She determined to think no more of him, yet immediately caught herself listening to his conversation with her host, General Dana.

Emily had begun to realize that this big-brotherly creature was of some influence when Nichols was banished. Well, after all, he was now a major general in the War Office. So what had that odd exchange between these two men meant? How could military rank be hollow?

At any rate, she was all ears when General Dana said, "I know for a fact that Lincoln was intending, at least up to a few weeks before his death, to *pay* the South for the slaves, up to 400 million dollars."

She gasped. Could the United States have raised such a sum?

Colonel Folsom mused, "Then the assassin, who imagined he was removing an enemy of the South, actually did them an enormous disservice."

Catching herself up crossly for appearing to watch and listen to this indifferent male, Emily firmly turned a shoulder to him. She began a private chat with Mrs. Dana about collecting clothing for the wretched Freedmen, and this carried her triumphantly back to the drawing room without another glance at him.

"How we do miss dear Frances Seward, don't we?" asked Mrs. Dana as they sat down together.

"Oh yes," agreed Emily with a deep sigh. "She was always so very kind to me from the time I was a small girl, and it was she who helped me first to get to Washington and then to endure here. I did love her so dearly, and I miss her so much."

"That assassin bursting into the house and attacking her menfolks, when she was so frail and her heart bad, one cannot wonder that Frances could not long survive it."

"No," agreed Emily sadly, "and then she had to die here in Washington, away from her home. But," and here she smiled tenderly though her voice wavered, "she had her 'Henry' beside her."

Then she went on, more briskly, "What does thee hear of Fanny Seward? I did find her at home one day, and thought she was in very low condition. She had been sick three weeks with pneumonia then, and said she had been ill most of this past year. Truly, I fear for her with the awful heat and the foul water here, and sicknesses so prevalent."

Mrs. Dana mused, "Poor girl, she never got over that terrible night, did she?"

"No, but think of it, there she was, right by her father's bed, with that maniac striking out with his knife! Even after a year, Fanny told me she cannot get it out of her mind. And then to lose her dear mother to the shock of it, as well." Emily shook her head over the harrowing account Fanny had given her.

The doors opened now and the gentlemen rejoined them. Major General Dana came to Emily to say, in his pleasant easy way, "You were about to tell me why you are letting the colored preacher hand out those seeds of yours. That surprises me."

"It shouldn't, though. They've got to start depending on their own leadership. I am turning over the distribution of the food and clothing allotments to them, too. I wish thee had seen their astonishment when the seeds came to view in their neat little packets. 'What a place that North is!' they said, and 'The Sesech never see the likes of that!' And I just want to boast a little about my families," she added, her face alight, as she saw that a few other friends were listening. "They have been so close in their economy, they have not been to the 'Drawing House' for funds once this winter!"

The others laughed at her eager pride, and she joined in with them.

"Well, Charles, what do you think of a woman who, all alone, is going to run a plantation?" asked General Dana.

"Oh no," she exclaimed, looking up quickly to find Colonel Folsom finally looking upon her with interest, "far from alone, with all my people with me."

The others were drawing back, not watching, buzzing among themselves, as the colonel questioned, and she answered, "Well, not really my people, but I feel them so."

The colonel's questions betrayed his sympathy with the freedmen and their problems. Emily found it just a little hard to get her breath to say, "This Freedmen's Village is going downhill apace. I have to shut my eyes to the hundreds of half-famished, half-dressed, overworked creatures, when I am powerless to relieve more than a few of them." Glancing up to meet those deep intent eyes, she added breathlessly, "I can do only a little in one place and a little in another. The need is bottomless, and it grows steadily more hopeless."

His deep voice prompted, "I am curious about your plantation."

"Well, I must explain, it isn't properly a plantation, for I am not buying the house and buildings. It's just my piece of a plantation. We'll have to build on it as we are able." She went on to explain about Uncle Moses Washington and Lewis Carter and Benjamin Tolliver, and how their plans included doing some chopping there this fall. Hence, as soon as she should gain title to it, they would "set sail to the Promised Land."

"And you are going to rent the land to them?"

"They are going to buy it from me, as they earn the wherewithal," she said proudly. "They are anxious that I lose nothing by it, and Lewis calculates I should 'make right smart of money' with their management."

"Bravo! I like your plan. Alms solve nothing, open no opportunities. This may answer." He added thoughtfully, "If I could be of any help to realize it, I should be most happy."

She would have liked to hide the deep pleasure she felt, but she could feel her face glowing.

At the end of the evening, as she drew her pelisse about her shoulders in Mrs. Dana's room, her hostess asked, "Have you heard anything from Mollie Martin?" At Emily's enquiring look, she continued, "I am so anxious about her. You did not know the lieutenant has turned out to be a gamester?" Seeing Emily's dismay, she continued, "We fear he will squander her entire fortune."

Emily exclaimed angrily, "And because she is a woman she has no recourse whatever. Is this not a perfect illustration of our biased laws? That poor, poor girl!" Shaking her head sadly, she turned aside to find her bonnet.

"Oh Emily, we are planning a day trip down the Potomac to Point Lookout in a couple of weeks. Could you not spare us a Saturday?"

Mrs. Dana did not say who the other guests would be. *Surely Colonel Folsom would be too busy,* thought Emily. She must admit to herself, she would enjoy the chance to talk with him at length about her plans. But there, she must be sensible. He was merely a very congenial gentleman with an exceptional understanding of the Negroes' problems.

Nevertheless as she picked up her bonnet, she looked at it ruefully and sighed, "Now I am paid out for being negligent about my wardrobe. I wish I had a prettier bonnet to wear down river."

Mrs. Dana immediately offered, "I have quite a pretty one which does not suit me."

It was very pretty indeed, and when Emily tried it on, Mrs. Dana exclaimed, "How very becoming, Emily! You must let me give it to you."

"No," she said, wistfully, looking at her reflection in the mirror. "That person looks far too dressy for plain Emily Howland. I shall write to Hannah. She knows just the right way to trim a bonnet for my taste."

She immediately wrote off to Hannah for a bonnet. Then, nibbling at her pen and thinking of dressing up her best outfit in the latest mode, she added, "I have a fancy for possessing a fanciful white apron, 'tis of small consequence tho'."

If the bonnet Hannah sent was not quite as becoming as Mrs. Dana's, the colonel apparently saw no deficiencies. He stood at Emily's elbow at the railing of the excursion boat, amid the gay music and jolly company. Even as they compared the merits of the two properties she was considering, the colonel's eyes were resting appreciatively on the bonnet as well as the sparkling face it framed.

Once, when she was finding it hard to meet his intent eyes, her own fell to the eagle insignia on his shoulder. This reminded her of

General Dana's tantalizing remark about "hollow rank." What could that have meant? Never mind, she could not ask such a question of a gentleman who was still virtually a stranger.

Since they were now nearing Port Lookout, she gestured across the Potomac to the Northern Neck. "There, the tracts must be almost opposite us." Then, her face clouding, she added, "My worry now is that Father says I must get the property surveyed. Can thee advise me on how one gets a survey made?"

The colonel's eyes crinkled. "There is nothing easier. Did no one tell you that I am a civil engineer, at your service, ma'am?"

Her face lit up. "Thee means thee can do it for me?"

"I certainly can." Again he bent the warm gaze upon her, which always had the odd effect of making it hard for her to breathe. "Most of my work has been with railroads in Nova Scotia and several states, but this would be no trouble at all. When you settle on which tract you want, I shall be happy to go down and survey it for you."

Suddenly feeling that this man was no stranger to her, she said as lightly as she could, "Ever since we met, I've been puzzling over General Dana's words about 'hollow rank.'"

He laughed. "I do not wonder, for it is an incomprehensible policy. Well, when I attained the rank of captain in '65, I simultaneously became a brevet colonel."

She protested, "Two ranks at once? How can that be?"

"Well might any sensible person ask," he said, dryly. "For I wear the insignia and receive the title of colonel, and I have all the authority and all the duties belonging to that brevet rank." And smiling at her puzzled face, he added, "But our grateful country *pays* me as a captain, my permanent rank."

Recovering from her first astonishment, she exclaimed indignantly, "But that is not just!"

His eyes twinkled. "I wholeheartedly agree. However, our army during wartime was full of such jumped-up officers."

As she looked her enquiry, he went on, "I was first promoted because Colonel Meyer, quartermaster for our depot, was killed. Then my immediate superior, who should have succeeded him, was removed from his post. Suddenly, there was no one but me to step into the colonel's shoes."

And with a grin, he added, "And if his superior had suddenly died, I expect I'd be a general in the War Office today, and still not a dollar richer."

Though she had noted and appreciated his lighthearted acceptance of this oddity, she still pressed earnestly on. "Then some officers receive much more pay than others of the same rank and responsibility?"

"That is correct."

"Who could ever have had such an idea?"

"I could not say, but," he declared, assuming a mock boastful manner, "President Lincoln himself signed the order granting me the title of colonel, for as long as I am in the regular Army."

Frowning, she said, "Well, this is not the first time I have disagreed with some plan of his." Then, her face clearing, she said stoutly, "But if President Lincoln conferred that title upon thee, then I know thee well deserves it."

The smile of amusement which he now bent upon her was so warm that she had to look away.

The only tiny cloud over Emily's day loomed when Mrs. Dana complained of Mollie's husband to Colonel Folsom.

He looked blank. "Martin? I don't know why you say that. He is an excellent officer. He takes her about and as far as I can see, she has good clothes. What more could she want?"

"Larger activities, perhaps?" suggested Mrs. Dana.

He looked puzzled at first, then shrugged. "Oh well, I imagine keeping their quarters and feeding him fills her days. I know he's a prodigious trencherman." And with a pleasant laugh, he turned away.

Emily was quickly able to forget her brief discomfort. After all, he had spoken carelessly, without due thought.

Emily, of course, had never worn the deliberately plain clothes of the old Quakers, but after this pleasure trip, she found herself adding little touches of lace at the necks of her dark gowns. She did not admit to herself that she might be doing so to please the colonel.

Her high spirits, she told herself on the afternoon he came to Freedmen's Village to bring her the completed survey papers, were because she could go ahead now. With this survey and Father's $1,650 draft, she could claim her 350-acre "plantation," the first land she had ever owned. Why wouldn't she be excited?

The colonel brought not only the survey description but an exceedingly well-detailed map which she could send to her father. They bent over it eagerly, locating the features of the tract.

"Oh, Uncle Moses must see this," she declared. "In fact, I should like thee to meet him. Such a life as he has led, serving a hard master for sixteen years and twice escaping and being retaken."

"I most certainly must hear him tell that," he agreed, and then went on, "I interviewed the owner of your tract. He told me that, since the Yankees took his slaves and since he cannot work, he must live by selling off land. And he said to me that they never did make much money on the field crops; they made their money raising and selling the young slaves down into Georgia."

Emily first shuddered over that dreadful statement, then asked, "Why can he not work? Is he ill?"

"He is perfectly hale and stalwart." The colonel paused to smile at her puzzled face. "My dear Miss Emily...if you will permit me the use of the title I hear your people calling you?" He paused and she, blushing, inclined her head. "Well then, Southern landowners do no manual work. If he and his wife were to know how you have toiled, they would be sure you must be of the lower classes."

Emily protested, "Would they rather starve than work?"

"Their idea that the master does not work has been thoroughly ingrained, and you know, Miss Emily, how hard it is to go against one's early training."

Oh, indeed she did know that!

He added thoughtfully, "It is hard to know what is really one's own conviction and what was graven on the mind in earlier days, which perhaps no longer applies."

She stared into space. This came very close to the heart. Suddenly, she realized he had turned to look at her in surprise and, even as she hurriedly agreed, she could feel her color rising.

He did not miss this, she feared, for his gaze lingered. Then considerately turning the subject, he suggested, "I should like to visit the Freedmen's village and particularly to see your school. Could we do that?"

"Oh, yes, I should be most happy," she said, relieved. "We must hurry, though, if thee is to see everything before the light goes."

As they set off, she explained, pointing, "Thee sees there the garden plots. If anyone says these people are lazy, I wish they could have seen this ground when they came. Thee would have thought it was paved with stones. They scrambled about picking load after load after load of rocks. And then they hoed night after night to loosen the soil. And now thee sees these beautiful gardens."

Looking about in surprise, he said, "But you said before that it is hopeless here."

"And so it is. There's no outside work to be had, and the aid societies in the North have disbanded, imagining the need ended with the war. And come October, all government rations will end. I've heard people say, 'As long as you insist on feeding the indigent, you'll have them to feed. Let them alone and they'll die off or go away.'"

They had stopped now and he was looking down at her with knit brows. "I had not realized the callous neglect of these people."

Encouraged, she continued earnestly, "So many hungry people! Uncles and aunties arrive just at my breakfast hour, having walked five or six miles without a bite. Think of it, hundreds of people around us half famished. I wonder they don't get wolfish and pounce on everything edible. But they just go on starving in the most dignified way. I can do almost nothing to help them."

She shook her head in distress. "So thee sees why I want to offer to a few families the opportunity the government should be providing for all."

He looked at her thoughtfully, then repeated, "I should be proud to help in any way I can."

She smiled gratefully, then urged, "Well, we must step along."

How pleasant it was, swinging along together, although she trotted now and again to catch up to his vigorous strides. His keen gaze noted every detail, and his questions proved his interest to be genuine.

She pointed out the village store, the barracks and cabins, and last, her schoolhouse. There she stood by her desk and addressed him, on the front bench. "Now colonel, let me hear thy times tables. Start with eight times one and continue to eight times twelve." As they both burst into laughter, in the back of her mind she was realizing she had never met such unfailing pleasantness and approval of her doings.

As they walked back across the commons toward the stable, he stopped abruptly. "Do I hear music?"

"Oh yes, it sounds like one of their impromptu evenings. Do come; they won't mind."

Clustered around a fiddler were dozens of people of all ages, in motley garments and children in broken shoes or barefooted. All were swaying and clapping and singing around the few exuberant dancers.

The colonel watched, tapping his toe, while she, with her hands to her throat, felt somehow anxious.

As they finally walked away toward the stables, the colonel remarked, "They really are musical. That was fine."

Emily said, in a small voice, "It frightens me."

"Frightens you!" He stopped and turned to her. "What do you mean?"

"I don't know them when they do that. They are not the same people." She lifted perplexed eyes to his.

He knit his brow and finally said, "They cast off their cares, do they not? They abandon themselves to their music, and that is foreign to you. I expect restraint was part of your early training."

She studied this, then nodded. "I believe thee is right."

He untied and led out his horse and stood smiling down at her in the kindest way.

"I should have liked thee to see the other schools in my circuit, but we would really need to go on horseback. It would take too long to walk, and I feel certain thee would not like Uncle Jacob's old cart."

He chuckled. "I also feel certain I should not." He swung himself into the saddle and she stood looking up at him. "I expect I shall see you at the Danas' before you leave for Sherwood. You are to come to them, the first night of your trip, are you not?"

When she met him at her friends' Washington home, she greeted him gaily, "Uncle Moses and Company sailed to the 'Promised Land' in the steamboat *Columbia* last week!" Then the entire company began asking her expectations for the plantation's first winter.

Someone asked, "Aren't you going to give it a name other than the 'Promised Land'?"

She passed this off, but later asked the colonel, "Thee has seen it. What name would thee suggest?"

His eyes looked faraway, remembering. "It was so green and sylvan and peaceful there, 'Arcadia' came to my mind."

They smiled at each other as she exclaimed, "Arcadia! The Greeks' pastoral land of idyllic happiness. 'Tis perfect."

The moment she was to remember all winter, however, was when he took her hand in his at parting, their eyes clung, and there were no words at all. At last he said, "Until spring," and she could only smile and nod at him.

Emily's winter chore of caring for her petulant and demanding mother was lightened by encouraging reports from her three families at Arcadia. Whenever she read one of the laboriously printed letters from Ella or Uncle Moses, she remembered her last view of them. Each of the dark faces in the long row at the railing of the steamer had been smiling, but the most brilliant had been the smiles of Uncle Moses and Ella.

The girl had been holding her two-year-old Lewie and waving his hand at Emily for him. He was twisting about, trying to see everything on deck, and squirming and kicking to get down.

"Oh, tie that boy to something or he'll be overboard," Emily had called urgently, between blasts of the boat whistle. Lewis, laughing, had plucked the young rascal from his mother's arms and, holding him in a vise-like grip, bellowed back, "If they got an anchor, we'll tie him to that!"

It was a most charming memory, that all of them had been laughing and waving joyfully as the boat pulled away.

She also had a letter from Colonel Folsom about the windows she had wanted for a school building, to serve both Arcadia and the neighboring village of Heathsville. He wrote that he had arranged for them to be sent, plus a gift of several more for the new house she intended to build there for herself. Knowing she would feel indebted, he added lightly that it was:

> ... little enough to do, and there is no danger of my going to heaven too easily by hanging my benevolence in this way on lines that other people have stretched.

For some reason she held the letter a few moments before reluctantly laying it away and going back to her mother's room.

There were plenty of winter evenings when she sat by the fireside conversing with Father, and William might step in and join them. Then the talk often turned to William Seward's interest in buying Alaska. Was it worth any such figure as the seven million and more dollars that Russia demanded, for a frigid land occupied only by a few "Esquimaux"?

"They call it 'Seward's Ice Box,'" William pointed out, one evening.

Father, with his canny eye for investments, especially in real estate, answered, "I believe it will prove worth the risk, William."

Emily put in, a smile twitching at her lips, "When thee met Secretary Seward in Auburn last week, Father, did either of you mention it?"

"Well, yes," admitted Father, "he did ask me and I advised him of my view."

Had Father's "slight madness" for buying land even faintly influenced William Seward to buy a great icy bargain? Emily chuckled irrepressibly at the thought, William grinned broadly, and even Father had to smile. He added indulgently, however, "Now, children, you well know that William Seward has long wished to acquire several such territories, with or without my concurrence."

In April Emily heard, to her dismay, that the Freedmen's Bureau intended to take over her school at Arcadia, and had already sent $200 for supplies. At all cost, Emily must give over nursing her mother and hurry back before she lost control of it to that bumbling federal agency.

1867

And now, from her arrival at Arcadia in April, began what was to be the happiest summer of Emily's life. She boarded with her friends, the Nashes, and from there she walked to her temporary log school. The thirty or so colored students who crowded into the little building daily were so eager to learn, without the usual jostling or tricks, that she wrote:

> *It seems to me that I must hitherto have taught a reform school.*

After school each day she consulted with Uncle Moses on the farm management. Then she met with Uncle Aleck Day on the construction by colored volunteers of the new 26' x 40' school, planned to be airy and well-lighted. Before supper, she taught the women to sew and mend and bake. Then she closed her day by teaching more than forty adults, both colored and white, many of whom had walked miles for an evening hour of the three R's. And for Emily's Sunday School, more than one hundred crowded into the same log building.

A particular joy was meeting Ella at church, still thin from hard work, but proudly wearing a most beautiful hat. She and her husband broke into delighted smiles when they saw Emily. Little Lewie, sitting between them, acted quite civilized, to her relief. After church, when Emily saw Ella's figure from the side, she breathed, "O dear," but only to herself, for the girl looked completely happy.

During her first month there Emily wrote Hannah:

> *Northumberland, Va*
> *May 21, 1867*
>
> *While quietly pursuing my busy way, echoes of gossip intimate I am the exciting topic in this region, a person about whom there are decided and antagonistic opinions, probably the best abused and best praised woman in the county.*
>
> *My supposed presence in one of the Heathsville churches caused a slight stampede.*
>
> *(One of the residents had been to Baltimore and got so fine a rig all thought she must be the "school teacher.") It*

*is amusing that they imagine me so grand. I am glad they
do, it gives the cause prestige. When I appear I shall most
certainly put on my best.*

*I never meet anything but civility. They say their spite-
ful things out of my hearing. Uncle Aleck and I have
marked out the ground for the church and school building. I am pushing them to get it up, we are so crowded. He
intends to have it called the "Howland Chapel." I would
like far better that it were "Howland School." A school is
what I would like my name perpetuated by.*

Aff. Emily

Soon she wrote her parents:

June 3, 1867

*Ben wrote me that father had conferred an income on
me which is certainly very acceptable and I am thankful
for it. The first year is the close time, of course. Everything has to be bought.*

Ben had also written that Mr. Backus had become president of
the bank and planned to put the entire operation under the Backus
family.

Oh dear, this put a period to any advancement for Ben in that
bank. Whatever would Louise say? But Emily would not mention
this worry to the homefolks. Instead, she continued cheerfully:

*The event of today is the coming of one of the "po'
whites". It took no little heroism on her part. I gave this
child a dress and some old shoes to make her as present-
able as she wished. I intend this to be a public school
ultimately.*

The only schools here on the Northern Neck had been the plantation schools. Consequently, most of the whites were unlettered. But
that even one should crave schooling enough to consider attending
with Negroes underscored the crying need for more schools, open to
all.

Thus, Emily thought of a friend from her winters in Philadel-
phia, who had since been acting as tour manager for the dramatic
Sallie Holley's antislavery lectures. Now that Abolition had come,
Carrie's work was done.

As Emily wrote to Carrie Putnam, proposing that she open a
school here, she visualized her friend: plain, efficient, somewhat
eccentric, yet acute—a dear old stick. She would be just the person,

if this plea could lure her south. And Carrie always craved to "do something."

For Emily it was idyllic, that happy and fruitful summer. She began to walk barefoot to and from school, putting on her stockings and shoes at the schoolhouse door. As she squished along the muddy road, she sometimes smiled to think how horrified Mother would be, or if she knew that, on hot nights, Emily slept under a tree in Nashes' yard. For a few brief months, there was no one to disapprove of anything she wanted to do.

And to add to her freedom and pleasure, Colonel Folsom had located a gentle gray-roan gelding for her to ride on her longer jaunts. During his unusually long stretches of off-duty this summer, he roomed with a neighboring gentleman. Thus, he frequently rode with her.

To her parents she wrote:

> *My horse—Well, I think he is as near perfect as father does Fan. He suits me exactly, gentle, a perfect saddle horse, good and good looking. Tom, who takes care of him and is very proud of him, says, "if he was his hoss no $200. would get him."*

One Saturday, Emily and the colonel stopped to water their horses at a forget-me-not-bordered pool in a roadside stream. He remarked, "This would be an ideal spot to eat that saddlebag lunch of yours." So, as he watched, lazily sitting against a shady tree, she set out their picnic. They ate it, companionably chatting or being silent with equal ease.

Once, she remarked, "I am so grateful to thee for finding Prince for me. He is a delightful mount."

"I'm glad he suits you. He is a lady's horse, of course. For myself, I prefer a mare. They have so much more spirit and 'try.' I do occasionally have to show her who's in charge, of course, but just a touch of the spur will bring her right around."

If Emily felt a little prick of uneasiness at his words, it was gone in a moment.

As the horses moved off to crop the grass, the dragonflies returned to dart and skim over the little pool. She finally remarked, dreamily, "I wonder what they are weaving?"

"I believe they must be weaving spells," he answered softly.

Startled, she glanced at him, able only to half-meet his smiling eyes before starting up to say, "Well, we must get on!"

Cornelia Hancock, the pert and lively nurse, broke her trip home to New Jersey from her South Carolina school with a visit. She required no urging from either Emily or Mrs. Nash to stretch her visit so she could thoroughly see Emily's "plantation," which held a fascination for her.

The two of them talked endlessly of their common interests: their new schools, their colored pupils, and of this settlement of Emily's where the Negroes could improve their own lot. The two women shared stories of their early lives, their families and villages and how their advanced ideas had frequently aroused disapproval.

Emily listened intently to Cornelia's poignant account of President Lincoln's visit to her hospital near Richmond to shake the hands, as he said, of "the brave men who saved the Union."

"There was a man great enough to be humble," said Cornelia.

However, Emily agreed wholeheartedly when Cornelia added, "When I think of the waste of all those fine young men, I realize anew that waging war and maiming men is not worthy of a civilized nation."

In all their talk, there was one person who went unmentioned. Cornelia said not one word of Dr. Frederick Dudley. Knowing of his devotion in writing and calling on her, Emily had no doubt that he had offered for her hand, and that she had held to her vow.

As for the colonel, neither of them opened any discussion of why he was lingering so long here in Virginia.

One topic they came back to repeatedly was the struggle for woman's rights. In a newspaper Cornelia had brought, Emily noticed a report of the hearing on suffrage for the New York Constitutional Convention. Emily had expected that spunky Elizabeth Cady Stanton would easily persuade the committee chairman, her old friend, editor Horace Greeley, to recommend an amendment for woman suffrage in New York.

"Oh, what a setback," exclaimed Emily in dismay. "Cornelia, did thee read this?"

Cornelia craned her neck to see. "Not all of it. I did see that Editor Greeley said to Susan B. Anthony, 'The bullet and ballot go together. If you vote, are you ready to fight?' She was a little sassy, wasn't she, telling him they'd fight the same way he did in the war, by sending substitutes."

"That was next door to calling him a craven who would not fight. But that's not the worst of it."

"And what is that?"

"The two of them, Mrs. Stanton and Miss Anthony, held back a huge suffrage petition collected by Greeley's own wife. They waited for his favorite saying, 'The best women I know do not want to vote,' and then presented this petition from *Mrs.* Horace Greeley."

Cornelia, who was now reading over Emily's shoulder, chuckled. "So, while the spectators and reporters hooted and roared, he turned red with rage and snapped that his committee would make no recommendation for woman suffrage. He paid them back for making him the butt of the joke, didn't he?" Then, grinning broadly, she said, "My, my, I wonder what happened when he got home that night." And again, more soberly, "So now they've got Editor Greeley on his high horse."

"Yes, and he's a man who will not climb down again. He hangs onto his grudges." Emily shook her head sadly. "It's very unfortunate, for so many read his *Tribune,* and he used to print anything Mrs. Stanton wrote. I'm afraid this will end it."

Cornelia suggested briskly, "Well, if thee knows either of the women, write and tell them... let's see. Tell them thee has it on good authority that a soft answer turneth away wrath."

Emily chuckled but protested, "I suspect they know their Bible as well as we do. In truth, I only know Susan Anthony by sight and I imagine Elizabeth Stanton barely remembers who I am, among dozens of women who've collected petitions for them." Upon thinking it over, she did sharpen her pen and write Mrs. Stanton modestly of her sympathy and regret for the rupture.

While she was doing this, Cornelia took up a wrap, saying, "I've been wanting to go and talk to Uncle Moses. That noble face of his draws me." And on her return, some time later, she exclaimed, "Thee wrote me about Uncle Moses, but not how he hid in a hollow tree for five days because it snowed and he 'dassent leave tracks.' Or when they had already recaptured him, how his master's vicious son quite needlessly shot him. Just as if he were a wild beast! Yet Uncle Moses tells me they were pious Methodists. Doesn't that make thee sick?"

Emily nodded. "I've seen him working with his shirt off and he carries cruel welts on his back from the whip. They must have deliberately lashed him to the bone over and over again."

Cornelia protested, "How could that dear man possibly provoke such a rage? He's such a worker, and so mild and so reasonable."

"I know. Treated rightly he would have done the work of two men."

Cornelia mused, "I suppose he would not be ruled by the lash and those brutes knew no other way."

Emily said, "Thee has said that the war was dreadful, but without it all these people would still be suffering such abuse."

Cornelia brightened. "That's true, isn't it? Well, that's all past, and Uncle Moses can't say enough in praise of Miss Emily bringing him to the Promised Land."

The next Saturday evening, an unexpected message summoned the Nashes to meet friends who were passing through the county. They rose to make an early start on Sunday morning. Just as he was about to swing up into the carriage seat, Mr. Nash suddenly clapped his hand to his forehead. "My land, wife, we invited Charles to dinner today! There's no way to let him know now."

Emily's spirits were suddenly dancing, but she said, sedately enough, "Thee forgets that I teach a cooking school afternoons. With Cornelia's help, I can certainly feed one man."

Mrs. Nash commiserated, "Oh Emily, that is just too bad. You'll have that huge Sunday School and then have to come home and cook a meal. And what can you make?"

"Oh, creamed oysters are quick. Cornelia can pick us a mess of greens, and let's see...I can stir up corn bread and slice some peaches. Now I had better stoke up the fire before we're off to Sunday School."

It was, somehow, a very special moment for Emily when the colonel pushed back his chair from the table and smiled warmly at her. "That was an extra fine meal. I never tasted better oysters!"

Cornelia chipped in, "Thee never had oysters in summer before, I daresay. We buy them off a waterman's wagon here at the door at twenty cents a bushel." Starting to pick up the dishes, she added, "But Emily gave them her special touch. Now colonel, I see thee fetched along a newspaper, so just thee read it while we clear up the remains."

"Well, hurry, so we can do something this afternoon, girls!"

"Now colonel," protested Cornelia, "thee may have done nothing yet today, but Emily taught the most gigantic Sunday School thee ever saw, and then hustled home to cook dinner for thee. She's been on the jump all day, so just settle thyself and read that paper."

When they reappeared, Emily was carrying a tin box.

"What's that?" asked the colonel, as he folded his paper and got to his feet.

"It's my specimen box. I am hoping we can walk out back where there is a swamp flower, the marsh pink. Some people call it the sea pink, and Uncle Moses says it is in season right now. I've missed it each year and I want *so* much to add it to my collection." She looked anxiously at the colonel. "I cannot find time to get back to the swamp during the week."

Cornelia cut in, "Do not apologize, Emily. 'Tis little enough to ask."

"Now girls, you can do that anytime. We can't waste my leave. I'm taking you both to tea to meet some of my friends at the Baxters'. They're expecting us, so get your bonnets on!"

Emily set down the vasculum on a side table, trying to hide her disappointment.

Cornelia had no such qualms. "Now just a minute, colonel! This is Emily's day off, too, and she has given up the whole of it so far for everybody else. Why should we not afford an hour or two for what *she* wants? Thee heard her say, if she does not get her whatever-it-is today, she'll miss it again this year." And at his expression, she smiled, "Now thee need not go looking pathetic. I have brothers and I know how they use that kicked-dog expression to get what they want from Mother. But it never works with me!"

The colonel's handsome lips tightened momentarily. Then suddenly, he smiled and said very pleasantly, "All right, Emily, if it means so much to you, I'll let you off this time."

Cornelia's direct gaze had not wavered from his face. Frowning, she commented, "I feel, colonel, that thee may be a rather hard man."

First his eyebrows shot up, and then his eyes crinkled with amusement. "One does not get to be an officer by being weak-kneed." Turning to Emily, he added, "What are we waiting for? Bring your box and lead us to this swamp of yours."

Emily's uncertainty melted under his smile and she snatched up her vasculum and a bonnet.

As they stepped briskly along the creek, the colonel's tea party garments were elegant compared to the women's serviceable skirts and heavy shoes. Undaunted, Cornelia remarked gaily, "Here we are, three carpetbaggers!"

Emily blinked at her, startled, and Cornelia laughed, "In the best sense of the phrase, of course."

Circling back afterward, with Emily's specimen safely in her box, they came into an avenue with many pines among the other overarching trees. "Oh, lovely," Emily breathed, stopping. "Look how the branches meet overhead...and those shafts of light streaming in at the end."

Stopping obediently, the colonel suggested, "The French would call this an *alleé*."

Remembering his remark later, she would be surprised and pleased at his knowledge of French. At this moment, however, she declared urgently, "I must make a rough sketch of this. You two walk on, if you like." And, sitting down on a fallen log, she took a stubby pencil and a small roll of drawing paper from her vasculum. "I never know when I may find a subject and will need these."

The other two stood watching her absorption. Then Cornelia, curious about why a convention of crows was cawing in the clearing, wandered off. The colonel sat down, leaned against a tree and tilted his head back.

Glancing up at the trees and back to her sketch, Emily mused aloud, "These pines are like the Negroes. Having it hard just makes them stretch harder and higher toward the light."

There was a brief silence, and then the colonel answered, "I think perhaps they are like you. You have overcome hard times too, have you not?"

Looking up quickly, she found him watching her with a softer look. She bent her head back to her sketch before answering, "Yes, I sometimes feel that I have been thwarted all my life, in anything I felt I must do. Until now, that is." And looking down the avenue, she added, "I feel that not only the Negroes are coming out into the light at the end of a dark...." She hesitated, looking for a word.

His deep voice again prompted, "*Alleé*?" When she agreed, smiling, he continued, "Your people did not want you to come down here?"

Still sketching assiduously, she answered, "No, and the hardest action of my entire life was breaking away the first time. After that, all else has been easy by comparison." After sketching a bit more, she added, lightly, "I take an uncommon satisfaction in being a carpetbagger."

"A carpetbagger?" He laughed softly. "No, not a carpetbagger. More of a dragonfly, I think." And seeing her surprise, he added, "A weaver of dreams."

Confused, she stole a look at him, then quickly dropped her eyes.

"Think of your dream for these people," he continued. "Dozens, no, hundreds, whom you've taught letters and figures and something of how to be self-sufficient in the white man's world. And take Uncle Moses. Cornelia told me what a nightmare he lived through, but now you've made his dream come true." After a pause, he added softly, "And he is not the only one."

Cornelia now appeared at the edge of the clearing calling, "It will be dark soon. We must hurry."

Before Emily blew out her light that night, she put a few finishing touches to the interrupted sketch. Shading in the sky, she left a star at the end of the pine tunnel... "*No, alleé*," she thought, smiling.

When Emily came in from riding to the plantation late the next Saturday afternoon, she found Cornelia in the kitchen preparing their tea. Pouring a cup for her, Cornelia asked, "Was the colonel over there?"

"Yes, he rode back with me. He and Uncle Aleck had laid out the drain field to the south of the latrines, so the men dug the furrows and threw in the crushed oyster shells." Emily tugged off her boots with a groan of relief and leaned back, cup in hand.

"That was not where thee planned to put the drainage field, was it?" asked Cornelia sharply, pausing with bread knife poised over the loaf, looking searchingly at Emily.

"Mmm, no," admitted Emily.

"Is it a better location than to the east?"

"Well, Uncle Aleck did not think so, I fear." Emily's mouth twisted wryly. Then seeing Cornelia's frown, she hastened to say, "He did not complain, and it is easier not to argue with the colonel. And after all, he had years of experience in engineering before the war."

Cornelia compressed her lips and looked grave, but Emily quickly defended herself, "Thee knows I have not time or knowledge to oversee everything. I am relieved to have him as a sort of partner in this venture, to see to the arrangements at both the farm and the school, even if I do not agree with all of them."

Cornelia was silent while she set out the conserves, but Emily felt her friend's vexation even before she argued, "He is a clever man! Thee does not imagine he is doing this for the fun of working, does thee?"

Emily, remembering the colonel's eyes holding hers as he handed her off her horse, slowly shook her head.

On her way to refill the teakettle from the bucket, Cornelia stopped with a jerk by the chest. There she stared fixedly at a folded sheet of paper which lay on its top.

Emily, watching absently, suddenly wondered what could be riveting her attention so long. Rising, she peered at it, also.

"Is that his writing?" demanded Cornelia.

"Yes, that's a note he sent yesterday to say he was back and to arrange our work today."

"That writing tells thee all about the man."

At that, Emily bent her head more closely over her address, on the paper. "I don't see how. Other than that his writing is big and confident." Here she opened the single sheet, turned it over and spread the letter out under Cornelia's eyes.

"Very dashing," said that critic, dryly. "Thee can also see he's efficient, for he wastes no effort on flourishes. Yes, and he forms his characters very legibly the first time so he won't have to go back and do it again, and yet his writing appears to flow fast and easily."

Emily looked at Cornelia, puzzled. "What fault is thee finding with that?"

"That's the writing of a man who gives orders. If thee will pardon my noticing it, he has informed thee, rather than asking, about thy plans for the day." She cast a sharp glance at Emily, then took up the sheet and said vigorously, "And look at the size of 'Your obedient servant.' Written that large, it's impudent!" She tossed the note aside. "The man is domineering!"

Suddenly, Emily laughed, "Oh, Cornelia, thee is a goose, getting indignant at a man for his handwriting!"

"He intends to swallow thee up," declared Cornelia as she replaced the teakettle on the stove. She then plunked herself at the table, waving Emily back to her chair, and pressed on, relentlessly. "Do I not remember, when we were wallowing about in the mud at the Freedmen's Camp, how thee declared thee would never marry? Thee was going to show our weaker sisters how to live freely."

Emily nodded. "I have vowed that many times. I still mean to hold to it. And yet our company together is so pleasant...."

Cornelia's face softened. "Yes, and thee has had all too little of pleasantness, that I know, dear friend. I am not blaming thee nor trying to take it from thee, so long as thee is sure where this is leading."

Emily was silent, absently swirling the shreds of tea around the bottom of her cup.

Impatiently, Cornelia reached over and, taking the cup from her, emptied the dregs and refilled it from the teapot. "I suppose thee is thinking that marriage would give thee a position in Washington and Boston society."

"I care nothing for position. Or perhaps that is not quite true. Thee knows what it feels to be always a nobody because thee is single."

"Mmhmm." But Cornelia continued mercilessly, "Thee does also realize that thee will own nothing. Thine income will go to the colonel, and he will support only the projects *he* approves of." Here she tapped the letter, now lying open by Emily's place.

Taking it up and folding it to form its own envelope, Emily asked, a bit wistfully, "Does thee dislike the colonel?"

"In truth, I like him very well, though he and I have no charms for each other."

"Does thee distrust him, then?"

"Not that, exactly. But remember that wretched Mollie who has never had any say from the day she married, and weigh what *thee* might also lose." She studied Emily's downcast face. "Thee is a strong woman, but he would break thee like a straw when the two of you differed."

There was a silence. Then Cornelia pursued, "Perhaps thee is thinking thee is not too old to bear a child. If so, remember thee would spend all thy talents on one man and one child, ending thy larger work."

Emily bent her head to hide her burning face. At last, she looked up and smiled tremulously. "I do not think this is real to me, Cornelia. In truth, I could not give up my commitment. I have held it too long for that. Perhaps I have been basking in a dream, just for a little while."

Cornelia impulsively patted her arm, across the table. "I know, dear friend, thee has had too much hard reality. Just be careful, it is a dangerous dream. He is a dangerously attractive man. And he plays on thy emotions. I saw the other day, when he let his face fall, thee would have given up thy walk to the swamp if I hadn't poked my nose in."

Cornelia's anxiety ended almost immediately, however, when a letter summoned Emily home to her mother's deathbed. Hastily finding a substitute teacher, Emily took the boat back to Washington, and from there she boarded the cars for home.

She waved to her friends on the platform until she could no longer see even the handsome, well-built man holding his hat aloft. Fortunately, she did not realize then that not only was this free and lovely summer over, but her teaching days were ended.

Bleeding Heart: "Hopeless, Not Heartless"

1867

Emily's mother did not linger long, but faded quietly away, as if glad to go. What were Emily's feelings now? Her mother had held her back from many ventures in her life and often Emily had resented her control. Now, standing by her mother's grave and looking back, she could see the usefulness of much her mother had taught her. Now she could more charitably realize that Mother had, after all, been trying to ensure Emily's happiness in the only ways she understood.

Emily could not leave her father desolate, so she settled in as his housekeeper and as Isabel's tutor. She began to conduct her affairs in Arcadia through letters of encouragement to the teacher Sarah Goodyear, to Uncle Moses who was overseeing the farming, and to Uncle Aleck Day, who was now directing the construction of her own new house there.

A letter followed her back to Sherwood. Elizabeth Cady Stanton frankly admitted that the scene at the Albany hearing:

> *cost us the friendship of Horace Greeley and the support of the* New York Tribune, *heretofore our most powerful and faithful allies.*

To Emily's regret, Mrs. Stanton did not suggest apologizing or making amends.

It was a full year before Emily again met the colonel at Arcadia. Though she traveled to the South in December, he was spending that holiday time near Boston, visiting his mother.

In her diary she recorded:

Dec 24, 1867: Home again in Sherwood. I was absent 3 weeks. Witnessed the opening of Congress. Spent a delightful week in my parish; the love and joy of my pupils to see me was cheering.

While she had been visiting in Washington, General Dana had handed her a clipping with a grin, "I saved this to stir you up."

The bad genius at the White House is working what mischief he can, so glad to reward the rebels and keep the loyal black men dependent by doling out charity. So long as the black man's rights as an equal are withheld, the South has won the war.

She handed it back with a shake of the head, saying sadly, "That's too true for jesting."

"Yes, of course," he agreed apologetically, and then added, "President Johnson is so anxious to heal the wounds of the Union, as he calls it, he is throwing away what our good men died to win."

Well, at least she had the satisfaction of seeing proof on her own Arcadian tract that the colored race, when given a chance to earn land, could well support themselves.

During her winter at home, to her joy, her good friend Carrie Putnam wrote, "I am always grateful when I am doing something in this world," and agreed to open a school near Arcadia.

Since Emily could not leave Father, she wrote to enlist the help of the colonel, who was back on duty in Virginia this winter. Please, she asked, would he help Carrie Putnam get settled in some kind of a building for a school in Lottsburgh, rather than "be idle as some society people were."

As she folded up this plea and addressed it, she chuckled to think of that independent woman, swathed in her shawls and indifferent to how she looked. What would the elegant colonel make of her?

And during that year, she also received a letter from the colonel which she shared with no one, but which she was to treasure for the rest of her life as "my letter."

At a family gathering at William's home, when Benjamin and Louise and their several children were present, Father revealed that he was sending Ben to Catskill, where he would learn the management of the woolen mill there, under a Samuel Harris.

Emily saw, from Louise's expression, that she was pleased at Ben's moving upward into an executive position. He had done well in the Union Springs Bank, of course, as Emily had expected, for he was a very industrious lad and sharp-witted as well. And he'd had years of experience in Father's woolen manufactory in Auburn. He should do well in Catskill.

For herself, it certainly was not welcome news. How she would miss Ben, her special friend and confidante. She had missed him, of course, during his college years, at first at Haverford, and later at Union College, but then he was always coming home to Sherwood for his holidays. Now with six youngsters, traveling would be no light matter. She could hardly bear to think of him living permanently two hundred or more miles away.

Therefore, it was with relief that she turned from her woe over this loss in their family circle to welcome Carrie Putnam, who was taking a short break after teaching six months at the Lottsburgh school.

After all these years, Carrie still looked exactly like a parrot, with her unfortunate nose. Never, felt Emily, had she had a less exciting friend, nor a kinder or more faithful one. She could have found Lottsburgh no finer teacher than this dear woman.

However, seeing Carrie swathed in her long, fringed shawl, Emily teased, "Did thee wear that heavy shawl this summer in Virginia, as thee did in Philadelphia in past winters?"

Carrie, unruffled, answered calmly, "What keeps out the cool will keep out the heat."

Emily chuckled, shaking her head. Her friend was just the same, unself-consciously going her own way.

Carrie spoke warmly about the colonel's vigor in settling her temporary school. "The lot Captain Wheeler gave us already had a building, but it was only a shell. Colonel Folsom recruited your friend Mr. Nash, and the two of them directed our colored people in putting on lath and a ceiling, and plastering the interior so I can heat it now."

Emily was delighted with this report, and the more so because she knew comfortably that they had taken no rides together. They had shared no "PicNics" by a shimmering pool. Still, Carrie's descriptions whetted her desire to see both the new school and her own at Arcadia. Yes, she was hungering for Virginia. And when Carrie began to fuss about Emily's dropping out of the work there, she was quick to say, "All right, I wouldn't mind revisiting the Promised Land."

Later she would report:

Georgetown, D.C.
October 30, 1868

Dear Home Folk,

At Aurora, we had the usual long waiting for the boat; on board, being chilled, we sat and drew our heads in like two old cats, until a feeble looking man with thought-lined face entered, whom Mr. Bogert greeted as 'Mr. Cornell'. They sat down before me and began talking of just what I wanted to hear, the University.

They were joined by Mr. Rooker of the New York Tribune. I suggested that Miss Putnam take off the old waterproof, which she did, and put on the new gloves. After a moment, Mr. Rooker brought Mr. Cornell and we embarked on a spirited talk on "Women and the University."

Mr. Cornell said, with a quiet smile, that he wished the young ladies who wrote to him had come.

He said, "Tell them to come next fall and we will be ready for them."

There is prejudice in the minds of the trustees, which two quiet girls by faithful walk and work could have dispelled into thin air. Mr. Rooker told us that Andrew D. White, the Cornell President, went to Europe opposed, but returned converted to the idea of women entering. Who knows but my nieces may go there yet!

Our three hour wait at the Bridge passed very differently from its weary predecessors.

At Geneva, we parted from the friends [whom] memory would hold long.

As she and Carrie traveled on down Seneca Lake, she had remarked on the pleasure of discussing their mutual interest with such a man as Mr. Cornell.

"So often it seems as though men and women are enemies."

Carrie, who was tucking away her handsome gloves, looked completely astonished. "Enemies?"

"Oh, dear Carrie, yes! When it comes to women wanting the ballot, men make it sound as though the women are being hostile to them—as though they want something special, when they only want to be treated the *same* as men before the law."

Carrie had still looked baffled.

Emily elaborated, "William Lloyd Garrison says it's time to change our demand from '*woman's* rights' to '*equal* rights.' After all, to be equal is all we ask."

Carrie nodded, but without much interest. As long as she could prepare her black pupils to claim their rights, Emily realized she did not care a fig for her own.

"I'm wondering, Carrie, what thee has heard of the Ku Klux Klan in Lottsburgh."

To Emily's surprise, Carrie had looked around furtively at the other passengers. Then she leaned close to murmur, "There is one. It hasn't done anything yet, but it makes my colored families uneasy."

"Thee must have some idea who they are."

Carrie had pursed her lips before saying cautiously, "Well, none of my white neighbors who once held slaves will speak to me."

Emily clucked, anxiously.

"They don't threaten, they just ignore me. There is a store where I can't get served. And I certainly would not try to go to the white church. These people call me 'the Nigger Teacher,' but that doesn't hurt me."

"Thee does not go out at night, I trust?"

Carrie had admitted, shamefacedly, "No, I dare not. And I had to give up the night school. It isn't safe for my people to be out after dark."

Carrie stood up here to shrug herself back into her waterproof.

Emily had watched her friend with mixed amusement and admiration for her indifference to her tatty old waterproof, and her natural dignity that raised her above it.

Emily looked back on this trip with some elation, for now she had met Ezra Cornell and had his commitment to admit women to his three-year-old university if she could find and help fund them. Emily meant to hold him to this promise, one day soon.

Arriving back in Washington, Emily cast aside all cares and spent a happy reunion week visiting the Danas and the Bowens. She also enjoyed the company and escort of the colonel, who had been mustered out of the Army several weeks before. She did not care to consider too closely why he should still be lingering on here. However, she and the colonel had immediately plunged into an eager discussion of affairs at the Arcadia plantation, and of his arrangements for materials for Carrie's Lottsburgh school. Therefore, Emily was quite glad at week's end to steam down the Potomac to the scene of all this activity.

She moved into her new house with Uncle Aleck's proud grin nearly splitting his head in two. "I never was so comfortable," she reflected as she sat by her hearth that first night, gazing into the wood fire.

The teacher, Sarah Goodyear, nervously hoped Miss Emily did not mind her presence in the house also.

"Oh, I planned this to be the teacher's house, but for myself as well when I am here. I never mind sharing quarters," Emily assured her. "I enjoy having people about. They interest me."

To Emily's enquiry about the Ku Klux Klan, Sarah belittled the danger. "Our white neighbors do resent our teaching the colored people, of course. Knowing their letters was always forbidden, you know. But with Uncle Aleck and our own men close by, we will be all right."

The next morning, Sarah set off to open the Howland Chapel School, as Uncle Aleck Day had insisted on calling it.

Emily, aiming meanwhile to step along to admire the properties of "her families," walked briskly down the dirt road. Happily, the handsome old trees between the road and the tidy cotton and corn fields had been spared to cast this friendly shade.

At length, she paused to look over the fence at Ella and Lewis's neat little home, with a glimpse of snowy laundry on a line behind. The door opened and the girl came down the walk, carrying her "last year's baby," Nancy, and wearing an obviously new dress and turban in a brilliant print.

"You remembering how it was, back up there, Miss Emily?" she asked, with a northward jerk of her head.

Emily nodded. Yes, she well remembered a subdued Ella, hoeing in her garden, with little Lewie tied on her hip, and wearing that ugly dark skirt from an aid society barrel.

"Well, look now!" Ella waved her hand and the two of them looked over the tidy little yard. Chickens were scratching vigorously, and little Lewie was hanging on the edge of a pen, watching a litter of piglets grunting and squealing and tumbling cheerfully. Even the porch on the little house looked as though Ella had scrubbed it.

Emily said sincerely, "I'd have known this was thy place if I'd never been here before, Ella. It looks first-rate. Thee can be proud!"

They smiled at each other, and then the young woman turned to show her finery before Emily's admiring eyes.

"*Beautiful*, Ella!"

It was true, the girl was beautiful once more; her smile was radiant. The dress also looked beautiful to Emily, both from the colors and from the prosperity and confidence it bespoke.

"Will you come in, Miss Emily?"

"Not this morning, Ella, but one of these times."

"Come along then, Lewie," and with an odd little bob of the head, Ella was off in a whirl of fashionably wide skirts and petticoats, hips swaying.

Emily watched, her head on one side and her smile deepening, as Ella bent to speak to little Lewie, and both of them broke softly into song as they walked along the road. She chuckled aloud when the two of them cut some fancy steps before they turned in under the big oak at the school corner, and disappeared from her sight.

"That woman was *pert* to you!"

Emily, startled by the stern voice, jerked about. The colonel, scowling darkly, had come up behind her, his steps quiet on the dusty road.

"Pert? No, no, she was thanking me in her own way. I like her to sing and dance and swing her skirts!"

He stared at her, nonplussed, and then grumbled, "You can't like those gaudy clothes, I hope? And where is she going in such a rig at this hour?"

"She's going to something at school, I expect, and I thought her clothes were delightful," Emily said defiantly. "That's her way of saying 'thank God.'" Searching his perplexed face, she added severely, "Now colonel, the whole trouble down here is precisely this attitude of whites, determined to keep them down, and wanting to take it out of them if they get 'uppity.' I must say, I expect better of *thee*!"

Taken aback, he had nothing to say.

"These people are working for themselves. Why shouldn't they be proud? That girl, Ella, by her own efforts, is on top of the world, and I like it!"

Looking down at her determined face, his expression softened into a reluctant smile. "Well, it will take some getting used to, but I always say, 'Miss Emily knows best.'"

They walked on pleasantly together toward Tom, who was waiting with both the colonel's lively, high-stepping mare and her own Prince. And again Emily felt, as she would part of the time during the next few weeks, that she had never been so comfortable.

At this moment, after her affectionate reunion with her horse, the colonel helped her to mount and then stood back smiling. "There, you remember I told you Prince is a lady's horse. A mare, after a year of standing idle and eating her head off, would have tossed you into these blackberry bushes." And, looking down into his laughing eyes, Emily thought, *What fun he is!*

As she settled herself into her side saddle, she felt her skirt pulling, and realized it had caught behind her stirrup strap. She reached down to free it just as he lifted his hand on the same errand, and their fingers met. How curious it was, she never remembered the touch of a gentleman's hand lingering on hers like this, nor the touch of any other eyes. Oh, dear, enough of this nonsense!

It was fun chuckling with him over Mark Twain's gibe about Alaska: Senators "ought not to spend millions in the purchase of volcanos and earthquakes and then retrench by cutting off the Senate's stationery supplies."

Somehow she was not quite so comfortable when she visited her school, although her pupils welcomed her warmly. They were so attentive to Sarah Goodyear that it was clear there was no need whatever for advice or help from Emily. She closed the door after her visit and trod down the steps feeling hollow and lost. Always before on any prolonged stay, she'd immediately launched into an intense schedule of teaching and supervising. Well, never mind, there was still the farm work to see to.

Lewis Carter and Benjamin Tolliver proudly showed her around their tidy, flourishing farms. Remembering the rags and squalor from which she had helped them to this prosperity, she felt an exquisite gratification.

And in the next moment, Lewis was asking the colonel what he thought of trying a few sugar beets and, when she would have put in her eager opinion, Lewis was shifting his feet uneasily. Though he was unwilling to turn his shoulder to her, he clearly wanted the colonel's verdict rather than hers. Only by a deliberate effort of will could she reason away her quick, hot resentment. How childish, when she had so much wanted these men to become independent.

She was warm in her praises, and both Lewis and the colonel beamed with pride. By the end of their tour, however, she knew there was no longer the slightest need for her here. All these farmers had needed was land and this chance to prove themselves.

She still had her own acres, of course, and Uncle Moses was meticulous in consulting her about her plans for them. Still, she knew he was quite able to manage without her.

Thus, it was with a lift of the heart that she heard the colonel say, as they reined in at her steps, "The next job for us is to do something about Miss Putnam's living quarters. Her school is habitable now, but that shack she's biding in is so decrepit, I don't know whether we should renovate it or just let the rats carry it away."

Carrie's school was nine or ten miles away, so they rode over to Lottsburgh early the next morning. There they spent a happy day, planning together how to make the dark airless two-room cottage more comfortable, with boards over holes, windows, shelves, and whitewash. The colonel promised to put the improvements in hand, while Emily undertook to engage and train an alert, biddable girl to come in daily for a couple of hours, to take the care of the cottage off Carrie's overburdened shoulders.

This ushered in another spell of happy activity for Emily. Sometimes she took a satchel of clothes and stayed overnight, to be on the spot to supervise the repairs and improvements, and to train the girl in tidy habits.

"She is competent enough," Emily explained to the colonel, "but this routine I want her to follow is so foreign to her that I have to remind her of some of the same things every day. I particularly want her to keep the ashes swept up on the hearth, so the cats don't track them all over the house. And as for these cats, I dislike sharing the house with them, but better cats than rats."

His laugh at this mild jest eased her discomfort over the way he had just overridden her intention of putting up a kitchen shelf. "Now you just let me take those tools, little lady, and you sit down here and watch," he had said, and had done it with neatness and skill. It was a pleasure to watch his big, well-knit body and clever hands in action. Unfortunately, she had risen that morning with the plan in mind for doing it herself. And yet, how could she be angry when he so boyishly enjoyed doing it for her?

This was not the last time he took jobs or decisions out of her hands. Each time, she felt cross and then guilty for feeling so, at the sight of him bent over a task undertaken to please and help her.

All these mixed feelings boiled up one evening as the two of them shared Carrie Putnam's supper. Twice that day, the colonel had taken the hammer out of her hand to finish the job she had started. Beans and smoked pork with cornbread was a soothing meal to her, and as her eyes went about the bright, comfortable little cottage as well, her irritations fell away.

They returned with a rush when the colonel answered a remark of Miss Putnam's. "I would not expect your girls to shine. Women's mental powers just aren't the equal of men's."

Emily snapped to attention. "Colonel, what can thou mean?"

He turned to her instantly, with a conciliatory smile. "Emily, you are the one exception. You do have a mind and interests to equal any man's."

"Oh, nonsense, I've been privileged. Most women act as society says they must. Forbidden an interest in politics and cooped up at home, how can they become informed? Given schooling and opportunity, they would be the equal of men."

He smiled, pityingly. "This is a point on which we shall never agree, my dear Emily. Now, what shall we plan to do here tomorrow?"

Emily cut in, crisply. "If thee will pardon me, colonel, this is a point which I am not willing to drop. I'm working with the Negroes so they can claim their rightful due. However, the rights of women are quite as important to me, and I hope one day soon to work for them!"

The colonel eyed her, his jaw very square. "You cannot mean you would take part in those scandalous performances, like those Bloomer women and the rest? I could never countenance that kind of behavior in *my* wife!"

Emily put her chin up. "I assure thee, colonel, I see no occasion for this concern. All thou must do is to choose a mindless little creature for thy wife."

"Now Emily, surely what is between us is more important than all that. You must see that."

Poor Carrie had fallen back in her chair, open-mouthed and clutching at the edge of the table. At this, she rose and fled.

"I would never interfere with your work with these people," the colonel went on. "I take as much interest as you do. I feel proud of you and I'm happy to help you foster this work."

"Happy to take it out of my hands, more likely," she snapped. Ignoring his bewildered, "What does *that* mean?" she rushed on, "Thee thinks a man has the right to say that his wife *cannot* work for woman's rights?"

They were standing now, he towering over her, and both forgetting Miss Putnam hiding in the kitchen in embarrassment.

"A man does have the right to say what his wife may do, and if she wishes to take part in unseemly public behavior, he certainly should forbid it!"

By this time, Emily was too angry to speak, and the colonel's face suddenly softened. Putting his hand to her hair, he said, "Oh, Emily, can this be you, hissing like a kitten?"

She jerked her head away. "Do not pat my head! I am not a kitten!"

It might still have ended differently, if she had not seen the quirk of his lips.

"Kindly go home now," she said, tightly.

Laughing, he protested, "But I'm eating!"

And now she was in a rage, past all reason. Opening the door, she ordered through her teeth, "Go away!"

Still chuckling, he took up his hat and strode out, pausing to say cheerfully, as he looked down into her furious face, "You'll feel better tomorrow."

She sank into her chair with knees that could hold her no longer. She looked up at poor shattered Carrie, peeping around the kitchen door, and then down at the three half-eaten meals. No, she would never feel better about his stand. He had resolved her quandary. Marriage was out of the question.

Clear as this decision was to her, however, the colonel did not realize it in the least. From the moment she had lost her temper, he had stopped taking seriously anything she had said. He insisted on treating it all as coquettishness, with an indulgent and maddening amusement.

The morning after the disastrous supper, she came out to meet him and make amends when he arrived for work.

"Oh, don't you bother your pretty head about that," he said, reassuringly. "You were just wrought-up. I knew it was not your intellect speaking. As long as you're feeling better now, we'll just put it out of mind."

It was futile, she knew it was, even as she was protesting, "Colonel, this is ridiculous. Have we not always listened to each other? Are we not two rational human beings?"

"Yes, of course we are," he answered, soothingly.

Despite his words, they no longer were. Something had shifted subtly. Emotions had surfaced, and he was reading this as encouragement. Looking at him in exasperation, she thought, "He is so wonderful, and so mutton-headed...and so impossible!"

The whole situation, in fact, was impossible. Before she could find a pretext to leave, Carrie Putnam borrowed a horse and rig and drove over to Heathsville to put a letter in her hands.

"I thought if you knew how much he thinks of you, you would reconsider his suit," she said, nervously.

Emily opened the letter and her eyes fell upon:

> *Emily's counsel will be best in that, as in all other things. She is inspired, you know. Isn't she wonderful?*

and further on:

> *She has the rare faculty of winning everybody's love,*
> *and at the same time making everybody mind her. A great*
> *soul in a little body.*

Emily folded it, and swallowed hard before saying, "Dear Carrie, I know he values me and I shall always have a great regard for him, I fear. Nevertheless, we would not do together. When neither can yield, how could there be any peace?"

And when Carrie looked as if she would say more, Emily added, "I do not mention it to give pain, but I could not *give* so much if I married. No, I must be free to give and to think and to do as my convictions lead me."

Carrie thoughtfully nodded her acceptance of this view. "Yes, I do not know what our schools here would do without your support and supplies."

The colonel took the news quite differently. When he realized she was going north, he blurted in bewilderment, "You do mean it!"

This soon turned to resentment, and she did not see him for the last two days before her departure. He told Carrie Putnam, who felt compelled to pass it on to Emily, that she had refused him for no reason at all.

He did relent and appear at the Coan wharf, as she was about to embark. Drawing her aside, he took her hand and murmured, "I have not changed. Write me when you are able to see more clearly."

It was a good thing she was leaving, for his eyes were so hurt and so loving, it was all she could do to get herself aboard. She wanted desperately to comfort him, but how could she do that without giving in?

As the steamer pulled away from the little group waving from the wharf, Emily could scarcely see him through eyes that were misty, for the pain she had dealt him, and for the end of the dream.

Meadow Sweet: "Usefulness"

1869

Emily had known that Cornelia Hancock would be too generous to say, "I told thee so," but Cornelia's reply to her letter ignored the colonel altogether. Instead, she plunged directly into her new idea for a second Arcadia on Cat Island in South Carolina. "Might thy father underwrite it, based on the success of thy plantation?"

What could be better than more freedmen earning land by working on it? And Father quickly agreed, if Cornelia could find a good cheap property. Only Emily, tied to Sherwood, was left out of the activity. And since housekeeping alone was never occupation enough for her mind and heart, she was soon restless. Carrie Putnam's next letter brought no relief, for the colonel had written crossly to her about Emily's stubbornness when once she set her mind. The colonel felt that he should not help with any Lottsburgh school repairs using Emily's funds, yet he could not pay for the materials himself.

Again, Carrie enclosed an earlier letter from the colonel which she hoped would soften Emily's heart:

> *I felt really ashamed to be trying to coax three or four stout men to do half a day's work each, when I felt as if I* ought *to and knew I* could, *come north and earn the sum required for them twice over in the same time. But Miss Emily says that* will not do, *and she knows, and what she says is law.*

Carrie added her own plea: "His position in the office of the quartermaster general in Washington ties him, but without enough to do. He always says anyone giving him a real object of hearty, useful work is his benefactor."

This would not do. Carrie obviously hoped to mend at least the working partnership between her two friends. Emily wrote firmly that she would sometimes contribute, but her active work there was done. And the colonel? She made no mention of him to Miss Putnam. Privately, she was sure he would return to Cambridge where his mother lived, and comfortably resume his life as a civil engineer. And somewhere in Boston, there must be a pretty, pleasant and conforming young woman who would soon erase Emily from his memory.

At this thought, she crossed over to her bureau, over which she had pinned up her sketch of the pine woods at her plantation. After studying it for some moments, she took it down and rubbed out the shading at the end of the avenue and with it, the star.

Her edgy feelings about the colonel, and her doubts about Ben's marriage, led her to write to a friend, at the announcement of a fall wedding:

> *I do not enjoy the prospect of people's marrying. I know it is human nature, but it seems little else than an increase of misery all round to most.*

And now the years began to fly by, "swift as the weaver's shuttle," as she wrote in her diary. To these stout little volumes she was to confide her doings and her concerns through much of her life.

It was a special pleasure to use some of her hours to tutor Isabel, and also to see the wonders of nature afresh through the eyes of the child.

"Oh look, Aunt Emily, a red toadstool!"

"So it is, Isabel. Oh, look here, does thee remember, thee used to call these 'collarpitters'?"

With serious dignity, Isabel reproached her, "That was when I was just a little girl."

Her niece was a complete joy to Emily, quite unlike the girl's younger brother, Herbert, who, when thwarted, might wail, "Bad aunt! Should give me cookie!"

And if Emily asked, "Why should I give it to thee?" he would hammer with his spoon and yell, "Because I want it!" He might pout until Isabel, anxious for peace, would give him most of her own cookie. And looking at his triumphant smirk, Emily would reflect on the unwisdom of giving in to demanding people. It was certainly doing this willful little boy no good.

On walking to the Sherwood corners with Isabel one morning, Emily noticed workmen behind the cobblestone store.

Isabel cried, "There's Papa," and immediately demanded of him to know what they were doing.

"Come in and see, Isabel. They are merely repairing the cellar wall."

Emily eagerly followed the group down the outside cellar stairs and greeted the workmen, both Quaker neighbors. Quickly she peered around to see any trace of a formerly hidden room.

She caught William watching her with almost a grin. She snapped, "Oh, all right, William, I ask thee no questions." However, as his smile broadened, she unwillingly smiled back at him and added lightly, "Provoking old clam!"

In December of 1869, Emily traveled south, going first to her own school. Then, while visiting Carrie Putnam's school, she wrote Hannah:

Lottsburgh, Va.
Dec. 14, 1869

Dear Hannah,

   Tell Belle I have had some of the most delightful walks I ever took and seen beautiful birds, red birds, cedar birds and one day a very large woodpecker with a red crest. There is a charm about these pine forests in winter like no other walks I ever took.

   I was very glad to get Miss Hancock's unabridged dictionary for my school in Heathsville. Miss Goodyear was so anxious to have a dictionary.

   Miss Putnam sends love and thanks. She will send Belle and Herbert some chestnuts.

Emily was not only enjoying this visit, but was admiring the courage of her birdlike friend. Previously resentful, the white community was now enraged because Carrie had been appointed postmistress, unseating the illiterate white incumbent.

Emily read hostility in their sideways looks, as she and Carrie walked about the town. Were some of these aloof aristocrats the hobgoblins in white sheets who had once or twice terrified Carrie's dark friends?

Was Carrie never afraid? Emily's question was answered when Carrie received a letter from her friend, Sallie Holley, who was still raising funds for the American Anti-Slavery relief work with the freedmen.

Emily sourly watched Carrie's pleasure lighting up her plain face as she read. Emily had always suspected the dominant Sallie of taking advantage of Carrie's devotion, and letting her arrange all their tour bookings and lodging, while Sallie needed only to appear on the platform. But perhaps she was being unjust.

Carrie, looking up, brightly exclaimed, "Sallie says, 'Putty, perhaps I should come and live with you.'"

"Putty," indeed! Emily was annoyed all over again.

"I wish she would," Carrie said. "She'd be just the one to push for the funds this school needs." As she folded the letter away, she murmured, "I'd feel safer, too."

Emily's ill-feelings evaporated. So Carrie was not so intrepid as she acted. And this was a very lonely life for her, seeing only her dark friends and the surly whites who collected their mail from her. Of course she would want her good friend's help and company.

Before Emily was to leave, she heard that a delegation of colored men from nearby Kinsale had asked for a teacher. Knowing the dawdling superintendent of Education, she decided to teach there for three months, while pushing the authorities to give these people aid toward a suitable building. She wrote in January to an aunt:

> *Thee may have heard by way of home that they had consented to let me stay the winter and start another school. I have fairly embarked in teaching for three months here.*
>
> *Last Tuesday Miss Putnam and I walked over here carpet bag in hand, from her school, a distance of nine miles. Blackboard and little household gear had preceded me.*
>
> *She went back the next day leaving me. The end of our walk was the home of a family. He is a white man to the eye but has a taint of color in the blood. This man has built the little school house and gives shelter to the teacher. It is a large family, 8 at home.*
>
> *My domestic affairs would be simply dreadful to a well-regulated mind intent on comfort. I have no room by day or night to myself. But I mean to be so busy as to be oblivious to all. I have baked some bread, only corn meal is eaten here, and with a cup of milk and some stewed peaches & tea, I fare very well. The wife is an excellent woman, seems painfully conscious that I am used to different things.*

Emily repeatedly saw, to her surprise, how warmly the Southern whites liked the very colored people whom they had exploited. Southern gentlemen often leaned from the saddle to shake hands with their colored friends. As a people, the Negroes suited their former owners, even while the whites resented their receiving the ballot and schooling. And ex-slaves spoke proudly of their former masters and mistresses. She felt ashamed for the Northerners who sometimes showed such dislike and prejudice toward them.

She wrote in her diary:

All these things are but for a season. One sees that the two races will work out the problem together.

She was also ashamed of her involuntary rush of gladness when Cornelia wrote that Mollie's arrogant young wastrel of a husband had died when thrown by his horse. Her first hope was that he had not had time to gamble away every cent of the girl's fortune.

Cornelia had written, "On my way home, when I saw Mollie at the Danas', she said he never let her contribute tuppence to any charity. The poor woman did not say she was glad he was dead, but she declared she would never marry again. She positively snapped that she could see why every widower wants a servant, but why should any widow want another master?"

Emily's ire rose as she read on: "She is bitterest that she could inherit only half of the remains of the property she brought to the marriage. The rest went to her obnoxious sister-in-law who made her married life a misery. Obviously all judges are men. So now Mollie is in straitened circumstances."

One last Cornelia-like touch tickled Emily, "It was an expensive experience, but she gained by it, in one way, for as a widow, she receives the respect accorded to a matron along with the freedom of a spinster."

Yes, that was true, Emily thought, as she packed her trunk to spend Christmas at her Virginia school. As a spinster, one could come and go as she liked.

Dec 22 1870
Heathsville Va

Dear Hannah

We are busy as bees preparing for a Christmas tree to bear all sorts of fruit for all ages and sizes. One box was filled with pretty hats for girls, gay with plumes.

There were toys & clothes for men and women & best of all 41 pairs of new shoes, besides a box of small children's shoes.

Here Emily paused, smiling as she remembered the arrival of the oxcart with five cartons. Especially delightful was the box of shoes in which two pairs were marked for "Miss Thomas" and "Miss Howland."

"I could just sit down and cry," the teacher had said. Then with a smile, she added, "We might better sit down and try them on, might we not?"

Emily had exclaimed, as they did so, "As many years as I have been handing out clothing, this is the first time I've ever been remembered. Norwich people are 'right royal givers'!"

And as they had stretched out their feet to admire these new buttoned boots, Miss Thomas had remarked, "The news of these boxes will travel on wings. We'll need packages for three times as many children as we usually have."

Emily smiled here. Miss Thomas' prediction was sure to be true. And how glad the recipients would be! However, she must hurry and finish this letter:

> *This a.m. a poor white came for the 4th time for my old shoes & I gave them to her, with a dress, a hood, and a little sacque. I wish I had brought more. Every patch and piece of all Sarah packed around my things is gone.*

Folding her letter, she wondered what sort of Christmas the Lottsburgh school had. Sallie Holley had come late in the summer and settled in with Carrie, after the Anti-Slavery Society had closed down. Her first comment had been that they needed a bigger school and a decent teachers' house "out here in the bush."

Emily had first sniffed with annoyance, upon hearing this from Carrie. But of course they needed new buildings. Perhaps Sallie could solicit the funds from her many Northern supporters. And now Emily could think of Carrie comfortably enjoying the easy companionship of her longtime partner and friend, the two of them standing together against the hostility of the community. Emily *did* hope Sallie would do her share of the work, and not expect Carrie to wait on her.

But even now, Emily wrinkled her nose as she thought, *"out here in the bush!"* And again, *"Putty! Whatever next?"*

Emily returned to Sherwood after her superb Christmas celebration with her Virginia friends, and resumed her "choring about the house." In her diary she noted:

> *I feel proud that I have earned wages and could earn my own living if I had a chance.*

Her winter, of course, was brightened by the frequent presence of Isabel, now leggy and endearingly awkward at twelve. She had always liked to show her new outfits to her admiring aunt. And Emily, who loved pretty clothes and approved of Hannah's taste, was delighted to see them.

Today, Isabel appeared in a modish kilted skirt and matching braid-trimmed sacque, with a saucy sailor hat.

Emily said tenderly, "*Mon joli oiseau.*"

"What does that mean?"

"My pretty bird."

Belle looked thoughtful. Then, turning slowly about, she asked, "What is a French word for my new costume?"

"*Joli*. Pretty."

"Oh, more than *pretty*. Stylish! In the mode!"

"Well, let me see. How about *recherché*, meaning sought after or in demand. It can also mean uncommon or choice."

"Oh, yes! *Recherché*. In demand! Choice! That's just what I wanted."

And as the girl left, Emily was amused to hear her rehearsing under her breath, "Recherché, recherché."

Still chuckling, she turned to the table and took up Father's neatly folded newspaper, intending merely to glance through it. Among the Cayuga County wedding announcements, her eye was caught by a familiar name: Dr. Frederick Dudley.

Startled, she read of the marriage of Dr. Dudley and Miss Sarah Slocum, both of Genoa. The item continued, "Dr. Dudley, much honored for his heroism in tending the wounded in the front lines, was captured and held in Libby Prison for four months. Soon after the war, he removed to Genoa, where he has since been a practicing physician."

Why, this was Cornelia's Dr. Dudley, living right here in Cayuga County! And married!

Emily dropped the paper. How proud Cornelia had been of her reckless young hero, how dismayed at his capture! Emily cut out the item, first thinking to send it to Cornelia. Or should she? No, why dim the brightness of Cornelia's memory?

She thought of Cornelia, faithfully teaching in her South Carolina school. Did that fully use the energies of a woman who had seen to the wounds and directed the feeding of a hospital full of men? Never mind, it was riches compared to Emily's meager opportunities to grow and do.

The next year she watched, with keen interest, the opening of a secondary school for both boys and girls just south of Sherwood.

Now Isabel would be able to attend school without leaving home. A Quakeress, Hepsibeth Hussey, had come from Nantucket to preside over this school and, to Emily's pleasure, she offered philosophy, botany, rhetoric, astronomy, and bookkeeping, as well as the three R's.

However, Emily, who had no part in this school which was operating under her nose, confided to her diary:

> *May 10, 1872: Still cleaning house. I rebel against the drudgery of my life. I found a beautiful lamp shade which someone gave me.*
>
> *I think it is so nice, I will send it to Col. Folsom who has done so many kind things for me.*

She held up the graceful frosted and hand-painted glass globe to admire its fluted neck, before packing it with care. She was glad to have something so special to offer the colonel, for surely he was a most deserving and generous man. Pausing to consider, she admitted to herself that he was, in addition, the most congenial gentleman she had ever known.

> *June 3, 1872: Ann Searing called, talked on science, theology, mental and moral phenomena. She sails for Europe to complete studies. Dear me, how poor my attainments and my career seem by comparison.*

Emily was currently bringing colored women from Virginia to her cousin's Howland Seminary in Union Springs. Ann's dashing career might overshadow this project, but only momentarily. Ten young women from Virginia over the years were to attend Cousin Robert's seminary. Several more would receive college degrees from Howard University or Oberlin, with her financial support.

Politics was a more absorbing interest than ever to her, in her secluded life. And now she raised her eyebrows when she read that brilliant, crotchety, arrogant Horace Greeley was running for the presidency against General Grant.

For thirty years, Greeley had been the most influential editor in America, leading crusade after crusade against slavery, alcohol, gambling houses, and any other practice which he deplored. With the *Tribune* for his soapbox, this should be a lively campaign.

With all this excitement going on, how tired she was of her housecleaning.

> *June 5, 1872: How foolish to try to keep pace with over-neat people.*

June 28, 1872: Had callers. All the ferocity comes out at a remembered insult. Lowell says, I think, that it is only his borders that are reclaimed, beyond is the untamed savage.

Sept 16, 1872: Our company is largely old men. They seem happy. It is conscious childhood, a second playday after the toil of active life. In childhood one is unconscious of anything else. I was not happy then, I was too much hampered.

Oct 12, 1872: What a puzzle life is. What a queer lot mine is. Hordes of people who care nought for me nor I for them, sweep thru our house pausing for food and lodging.

How much pleasanter life in the South is to me. There is a feeling of security from intrusion which is comfortable. Then there is no strain about living, in cookery or upholstery or dusting, which is all such a relief.

Oct 14, 1872: Mr. Seward's poor worn body was lain by the two dear ones. 6 years since his daughter Fanny left us. One of the most remarkable men of this century, yet not the equal of Mrs. Seward.

How strange it was that she, Emily Howland of Sherwood, should have known such a famous man, a man of such influence in the events of his time.

Nov 27, 1872: I read a little in Boston paper sent by C.W.F.

As she wrote this item that evening, she stopped and looked at the initials, smiling. But at the time, Emily had thrown the paper down in disgust. Though the colonel had earlier written pleasantly, thanking her for the lamp globe, he had still not been able to resist teasing her about the suffragists and their "antics."

Now he had sent this paper with a circle around a horrid item about presidential candidate Victoria Woodhull, who had just testified in a scandalous hearing on the indiscretions of the Reverend Henry Ward Beecher. This flamboyant and brassy woman had naturally not received a single electoral vote, and her affiliation with the National Woman Suffrage group was a disaster. What could possibly cast a worse reflection on it? Or be better ammunition for the colonel's mockery?

Emily's eyes, falling with distaste on the discarded newspaper, had noted another circled item as well, and taking up the paper apprehensively, she had read:

This was the strangest of election campaigns. Candidate Horace Greeley, who has long craved and maneuvered for public office, had not much more chance of victory than the audacious divorcee, Victoria Woodhull.

Rejected by his own Republican party which he helped to found, he was reluctantly espoused by the very Liberals he has so long and vigorously opposed. One can only suppose that they would have run the devil himself had His Satanic Majesty the slightest chance of carrying them to victory against that stolid hero of The People, the Republican incumbent General Ulysses S. Grant.

Nov 30, 1872: Word of death of Horace Greeley. I have not wanted him for President, nor liked his views on the woman question, still I believe him to have been one of the best public men and the ablest journalist of his time. He and Seward, names so long conspicuous in our affairs, are now passed into history.

Emily had gasped when she first read this news. Greeley *dead*? He had actively campaigned right up to Election Day just three weeks ago! Could such a fiery man, who for thirty years molded public opinions and events...could such a man actually die of disappointment?

A furious Elizabeth Cady Stanton had snapped, "Horace says this is the Negro's hour and we women must wait." Emily wondered, if Greeley had decreed that it was their hour as well, could his influence have won the women their right to vote?

Dec 10, 1872: A good many times I've been omitted where it seemed to me I belonged, or I've had to see others reap where I have sown. How keenly H. Greeley must have felt this. One is not anxious to be conspicuous but one likes recognition of one's good intentions or one's services or place.

Foolish heart.

Dec 11, 1872: Tried lard, made sausage, cleaned hogsheads, and ironed.

Later she would remark to Hannah, still her staunchest friend, "I feel for all housewives tied to a round of duties. No wonder they call it a *round*, since all their duties keep coming round and round again."

Jan 29, 1873: There is only the thinnest film between me and despair. I must keep out of the past. I am what I am, an old maid, the destiny I would not shirk.

Apr 14, 1873: Studied Etymology in evening. What a pity I had not kept on studying. I mean to see if I cannot recover some of the loss.

May 10, 1873: A long 10-leaved letter, genial and sunny, from C. W. Folsom. I did not think he'd ever write me again. No dyspepsia in his makeup. His letters make me feel as though I'd tasted some inspiring draught.

May 17, 1873: I am as neat in idea as my neighbors, but my better part revolts from being thus absorbed and I shall not.

Emily found herself yearning for the unencumbered life in the South, after a long winter of trying to maintain such a large house. With such a "muchness" of possessions and so many visitors to feed, all her duties stole her precious times of solitude.

May 18, 1873: I wanted to go to the woods with the young people but Father took a fancy to go to Augustus Howland's so I could not.

How hungry she had been to go with Isabel and the others to see the spring wildflowers. Yet how could she refuse Father, when he looked so disappointed?

As they jogged along in the buggy, Cornelia's words to the colonel suddenly came to her mind. "Thee need not go looking pathetic. I have brothers, and I know how they use that kicked-dog expression to get what they want from Mother." Stealing a sideways look at Father's serenely satisfied expression, she bit her lip and wondered.

May 19, 1873: My thirst for knowledge was never so strong.

In June, Emily avidly followed the reports of the trial of Susan B. Anthony on a charge of voting illegally the previous November.

The defense lawyer argued that the 14th Amendment granted the vote to all citizens of the U.S., and Susan was surely a citizen. "If her brother had voted, he would not be charged with a crime. Therefore she is being tried, not for voting, but for being a woman."

The furious judge high-handedly bypassed the jury. Declaring her guilty, he fined her $100 plus costs, which she flatly refused to pay.

The papers were full of this, and Emily had to admire Susan's courage. Still, she was not sure whether it would set the cause ahead or back in the public eye. But she shuddered to think what the colonel would say.

June 20, 1873: 15 different persons have eaten here within 6 days. Many callers also.

June 28, 1873: Went to H. Hussey's school closing. Exercises prolonged to weariness. Their effect is greatly injured thereby.

June 29, 1873: I don't like to feel that I may be invaded by company at any moment. I don't like the crowd forever passing thru our house.

July 5, 1873: Father bought a power churn.

One evening during this year, her father fetched home a bedraggled Harriet Tubman, the victim of a flimflam in Poplar Ridge where she had been chloroformed and robbed.

"Oh, Harriet!" Emily gasped, rushing to take her arm.

Though dizzy from the blow on her head, the valiant woman managed to grin feebly. "Land, chile, don't worry 'bout old Harriet! I's been in tighter pinches than that."

Hesitantly, Emily asked why Harriet, who was normally so shrewd, had believed the rascal had gold to sell.

"Some friends of mine *did* find a trunk of gold one time," was Harriet's amazing answer. "But your daddy, he's going to see what he can do 'bout it all."

It was true that Father and William talked seriously about "the Gold Man" and what recourse there might be. It fell to Emily to act as Harriet's hostess until she was well enough to go home to Auburn. Admire her as Emily had to, entertaining her was nevertheless a mixed pleasure, for Harriet was a very single-minded woman. She was oblivious when interrupting conversations, likely to be clomping about before the rest of the household was up, and not at all refined in her ways.

Now, however, Emily had a chance to hear about the nineteen forays Harriet had made into the South, leading out 300 slaves along the "Underground Railroad." She had carried a pistol to urge the reluctant and opium for crying infants, and all this time, the price on her head rose and rose, to a total of $40,000.

"Every bounty hunter in the whole East must have been searching for thee," marveled Emily. "However did thee elude them?"

"Don't know. Only knows I was told how and when to git."

Emily was now becoming caught up in the local problems. One of the worst was the abuse of their families by habitual drunkards. In May of 1873, though knowing it was futile, she addressed a letter:

To the Board of Excise at Scipio Center:
Gentlemen,

We bring a petition signed by 222 voters and 465 non-voters, asking you to grant no licenses for the sale of intoxicating liquors in this town.

We do not present so large a number of names because the bad roads prevented the circulation of the petition.

Some of the names are women and children whose husbands and fathers are in the thralls of liquor. A woman walked through some miles of mud to sign this paper hoping it might help save her husband.

The other day, a woman came to tell her woes.

She returned to her home from a day's work and found her husband in a raving state. He thrust her outdoors, knocked her down and kicked her, so that she was not able to work for a fortnight. He is a peaceable man when he is sober, she remarked. She had requested the landlord months before not to sell him liquor. She said, "I don't want to make a fuss. I only want him not to sell my husband any more liquor that makes a fiend of him."

In 1874, Emily received another letter from Colonel Folsom, now a civil engineer for the city of Boston. From this time they kept up an intermittent correspondence, but the papers he persisted in sending kept her aggravated.

He was put out, so he wrote, at the unseemly behavior of the women who, back in the winter, had mounted a Fifty Day Temperance Crusade. They had walked in procession to stand before saloons to sing and offer prayers. If a saloon keeper would admit them, the leader would lay her Bible on the bar while they sang "Rock of Ages." Women in saloons! It was disgraceful, he wrote.

This irritation was still in her mind when she and her sister-in-law were sitting together in the garden. Hannah ventured mildly, "Does thee never wish thee had accepted some one of the gentlemen who have admired thee? Would not marriage have given thee...."

Emily supplied, "Position? That is true. The world expects a man at woman's side. She is a cipher without him. Yet with him, she is but his shadow."

Hannah's gentle face puckered with distress, but she persisted, "If thee married, think of the companionship. And thee would have thine own home, for Father Howland would not expect thee to care for him then."

Emily was facing the sun, and half-closing her eyes against it, she looked about the garden, considering how to answer. "Well, then, Hannah, imagine sitting here with the sun in thine eyes, and thee sees what appears to be a rose arbor. Thee might rise and step into it, the better to smell the roses. What if thou should then find thyself in a cage, with roses on the bars but nonetheless, a cage?"

"Oh Emily, how can thee use such a simile?"

"Dear Hannah, is thee going to tell me that brother William does not make all thy decisions for thee?" Emily smiled to soften her words, for she would never willingly hurt this dear friend.

Hannah fell silent, then argued, "But thee has no standing. Every matron in the countryside takes precedence over thee."

Emily admitted, "Yes, women are welcome only when they are half of a pair. They have no other identity. I know people think of me as that odd spinster Howland."

"Well, then?"

"Well, Hannah!" she teased, smiling, and then continued more soberly, "I suppose I know what thee is suggesting. Certainly the colonel and I could be very pleasant together, but only if I would give up my dearest wish, to support the work for woman's suffrage. This I can not do."

Emily was to renew this vow over and over during the next years, as Colonel Folsom sent her bundle after bundle of Boston and Cambridge papers scoffing at woman's suffrage.

Did he imagine he could discredit the suffrage cause with his ridicule until she would actually give it up? Couldn't he see that every biased report made her the more determined to work for justice for women?

"Listen to this, Hannah," she might sputter. "Here is a new list of reasons why women should not vote. They are weak and delicate; their brains are smaller and more susceptible to mental illness. And here is the crowning argument: the vote for women is unnecessary as every man is influenced by the woman in his home!"

Or "Harken to this, Hannah. The colonel calls Frances Willard 'That Saloon Woman' because just once, during the Fifty Days Crusade, she went into a saloon. If she had denounced liquor without ever seeing a saloon, the colonel would say she did not know anything about it. Then he tells me that *we* are the illogical sex!"

In October of 1874, Carrie Putnam wrote from Lottsburgh, "Sallie says we are confounding the Virginia rebels over how our new schoolhouse has sprung up. It's almost done, and forty of our pupils are back after their busy summer hoeing in these immense corn fields. So we are busy."

Emily allowed herself a few moments of regret for the rickety school where the colonel had directed repairs. And even Carrie's shack, which the two of them had spruced up together, was now replaced by a cheerful teachers' house.

Carrie's letter continued proudly: "This is all Sallie's doing. She works from dawn to dark, between the house and her classes and the gardens. And it's her Northern friends who send the funds for the school, and the barrels of clothes for our people. She's a wonder."

Emily was surprised at this, and thoroughly ashamed of her former suspicions. As she read the end of Carrie's letter, her old feelings against Sallie vanished forever.

"When Sallie first flew our American flag with every stripe and star intact, the neighbors yelled that they'd shoot us and burn our schoolhouse over our heads. Well, Sallie went right out and stared them down, calling out, 'Shoot, if you want to, but if you do, the North will send a dozen more in our place!'"

Yes, what could Emily do but respect such a heroine?

In 1876, she read, to her disappointment, that the Statue of Liberty, promised for the Centennial celebration in Philadelphia by the talented young Frenchman, Frederic-Auguste Bartholdi, was not finished. Only the giant hand holding the torch had arrived. Probably the rest of it would never get done now, she thought, regretfully.

She was also uncomfortable about Susan B. Anthony's plan to march in and disrupt the great July 4th Centennial program in Philadelphia. Susan would present the "Declaration of Rights for Women" to the vice president on the stage, and her helpers would pass out copies, on their way back out of the hall.

Naturally, the colonel called this "unseemly behavior," and quoted Mark Twain: "Women are just not behaving like women anymore. Now is the time for all good men to tremble for their country."

The next year, however, the colonel applauded Clara Barton's campaign to start an American branch of the Red Cross for the relief of war wounded. "Now that is womanly work," he wrote.

The colonel also sent her a clipping:

Emma V. Brown, a graduate of Oberlin College, has opened the first colored public school. She is principal of a private school for colored children, as well.

He knew, of course, that Emma Brown was her friend and her former assistant in Miss Miner's Normal School. But he had no idea what pleasure Emily took from having encouraged and financially helped her toward this achievement.

Between times, Emily became active in local meetings and often spoke a few words, by request, at county reform society meetings. And in addition, she was overseeing her father's farms for him.

When Isabel entered the twelve-year-old Cornell University in 1877, her aunt was very sorry that founder Ezra Cornell had died in 1874, only two years after the first intrepid woman managed to enroll. How much Emily would have enjoyed invoking his promise for this intelligent, charming registrant.

Oddly, though Cornell's Sage College for Women had opened in 1875, and Emily had several times stayed there, and attended lectures on the campus during that year, she had not experienced the unpleasant attitude of the male Cornell students and staff toward the brave, bright younger women. The men were there first, they had seven all-male years before women were admitted, and now they bitterly resented these interlopers in their sphere. Emily, having missed all this, had the warmest feelings about Cornell and had written a note to a friend she had met there:

May '76
Dear L. Hoxie
   I love to think of my Cornell days.
   Love to Miss Johnson and to Miss Thomas.
   from thine
      Emily Howland

Thus she protested, when she visited Isabel on campus, at the girls scuttling along, making themselves small and inconspicuous, catching no eyes and speaking to no male. In class, they took notes but volunteered no answers, even when the men were at a loss.

After a class, which Emily had observed, she probed, "Did thee not know that answer?"

"Oh yes, of course," laughed Isabel. "And so did the others, but it would never do to put ourselves forward. We spend all our time trying to be invisible."

"I think this is frightful," fumed Emily.

"No, no, dear aunt, to us it's like a game. What we are getting is worth these little rubs, and we just joke about them."

Dismaying as this was to Emily, she admitted that an education was worth any amount of snubs or sneers.

Back in Sherwood, she longed to have a part in Hepsibeth's Select School, but that indomitable woman needed and wished no help.

Dec 4 1877: Went about with my Woman's Suffrage petition. Found no opposition. All took it as a good joke. Women might vote if they wanted to, certainly.

She was both irked and amused by one wife who answered the door, wringing soapsuds off her forearms and wiping her hands on her apron. Taking the petition and squinting at it, she then handed it back, saying scornfully, "I don't need the vote. I have a husband to take care of *me*."

Emily cast an eye over the crumbling porch and the litter around the yard and sniffed, as she untied her horse, stepped back up into her buggy, and unwound the reins.

It surprised Emily that William, with his big-brotherly eye out for any unseemly behavior, had never objected to her driving about with petitions. Though the two of them had grown closer with the years, he was not the friend and companion to her that Ben was. To him, she was still the little sister for whom he felt responsible. Hannah, who loved them both, would protest that Emily had never really known William, when she called him an old bear.

Dec 13, 1877: I am writing a letter to CWF.

Dec 23, 1877: I am hungering for something beyond me.

Dec 24, 1877: Christmas Eve. I never spent a sadder one within myself.

To cheer herself, she wrote many letters to her friends from Philadelphia days, now active suffragists. Among the streams of Father's elderly houseguests, visits from any of these special friends were wonderfully refreshing to her spirits.

Cornelia Hancock had written from London, the year before, about the innovative ways the English aided their needy. Now Emily heard that her lively friend was setting up a Family Society in Philadelphia, to visit and oversee aid to destitute families.

Cornelia also reported on the Cat Island plantation, which had cost Father $1,350 ten years ago and Cornelia herself $723. Though this little island, which could be reached only by ferry, had failed to attract colored settlers, still there was ample phosphate for mining.

Whatever Cornelia had felt for Dr. Dudley, all these projects certainly fitted her abilities better than being a village wife, Emily thought.

However, though she would not crow to Cornelia, it was a thorough satisfaction to Emily that several of her families had paid her in money or produce for land at Arcadia, usually at five dollars an acre.

March 11, 1878: Cut a chemiloon and prepared to make it.

March 12, 1878: Father received telegram: Cousin Sarah Alsop died. Packed my trunk all a.m.; left home at 3 p.m. Had to make some underwear. Moral, best not to sew for others even if they be orphans, and leave one's self unclothed.

March 14, 1878: Reached Philadelphia about 6 a.m. Took street cars & was soon at 301 8th St. The meeting appointed for 2 p.m. was my ideal of such an occasion. Lucretia Mott spoke very sweetly and sympathizingly.

After the memorial service, Friend Mott took down Emily's boarding house address, saying, "Thee will be lingering to attend classes? Then I shall hope to call on thee before thee leaves the city."

March 18, 1878: Went to Mary Grew's, to Woman's Club in evening, very interesting.

March 30, 1878: Lucretia Mott called. What a beautiful old age crowned her excellent life.

Emily had started up with a cry of pleasure at the sight of her caller. She held a deep affection for this modest woman who had such a mighty influence on the whole woman's movement.

First, of course, Emily reminded Mrs. Mott of the night her father came to Philadelphia and took her out of school. "Thee can have no idea how thee helped me by thy words of encouragement that night. Often in the years since, I would resolve anew that, no more than thee, would I let circumstances defeat me."

Lucretia Mott murmured, wonderingly, "My dear child!"

"And indeed," continued Emily, "the words thee spoke earlier that day have colored my whole life."

Friend Mott tried to remember, then shook her head.

Emily reminded her, earnestly, "Thee asked our school assembly who the *other* slaves were whose wealth was stolen from them, and who had no rights, meaning married women, of course."

"Oh, yes, I do remember. I spoke rather immoderately, I fear, for the rebuff Lizzie Stanton and I had received at that Anti-Slavery Convention in London was still rankling. They refused to seat any of the women there, simply because we *were* women."

"Thee only stated the truth, and it did us all good to hear it made so plain. Thee did not sound angry to me."

"I fear that I was. Even so, our indignation set off our Seneca Falls meeting in 1848, and all that has followed from it."

"How I wish I could have been at that meeting," sighed Emily. "They would not let me come, of course."

Lucretia Mott smiled, reminiscently. "One of my favorite memories is of Lizzie Stanton insisting women must have the ballot, and my complaining, 'Lizzie, thee will make us ridiculous!' Fortunately, Lizzie saw further than I. Her foresightedness has always been out of the ordinary way. We could not have done without her."

She mused on, "Lizzie grew up trying to be the boy her father wanted. She was tutored like a boy, and sat in her father's law office as a son might have done. Yet no matter how she excelled, he never gave her the rights and respect a son would have had, for a fraction of her accomplishments.

"I, on the other hand, lived in a female's sphere, never dreaming a woman could hope for rights equal to a man's. Only Lizzie had the vision to see it was both possible and right."

Emily mourned, "If only she had not clashed with Horace Greeley."

"Yes, Lizzie always has been impetuous and then stubborn. This is both her strength and her weakness. Still, her longer vision started the movement and has swept it along ever since."

Later, Friend Mott said, "It all comes back to me now, how fervently thee hoped to take medical training. I can still see thee at Mary Grew's fireside, with all thine ardent hopes dashed down, poor child. Thee did later attend the evening lectures at the new Female Medical College, did thee not?"

"Yes, for several winters," agreed Emily, "but my people would never have allowed me to train in earnest. I finally had to alter my pattern to fit my cloth, as the saying goes. I believe now that teaching suited me better, for I could help a whole roomful of colored people at once to better their chances."

And to this, Mrs. Mott nodded thoughtful agreement.

Before she left, Emily said wistfully, "Of all my colleagues, I have always most admired thee for shining in both the domestic sphere and on the public platform. I wish I might master the same."

Friend Mott paused on the porch to turn and say, with her peculiarly sweet smile, words that Emily would cherish, "Thou need not be modest, for thee has done a power of good for others in thy time."

Apr 7, 1878: Went to Germantown to hear H.
Longfellow. A fine sermon. The first time I ever heard my
own thoughts set in order and stated.

Apr 23, 1878: Miss Bodley asked us to go to the reception at the Medical College.

Apr 29, 1878: Returned to New York City. Bought a white skirt for 25 cents and a pair of sleeve buttons for 20 cents.

May 2, 1878: Visited a collection of antiquities. How small it made me feel to look at things made 4000 years ago. Our whole history was a speck in time.

May 4, 1878: Went to Catskill to visit brother Ben.

Dear Ben, how good it was to see him. After all these years, he was still the warmhearted boy she had always loved. And what a successful man he had become, as secretary and treasurer of the Hop O'Nose Knitting Mill, and director in the bank as well. When they walked together on the street, she glowed at the respectful greetings that her favorite brother received.

Louise's coldness, however, cast a cloud over this visit. How could she treat darling Ben so?

Emily had to bite her tongue when Louise said to Blanche, their eleven-year-old daughter, without turning her head to see if Ben was there, "Tell your father I want three tickets for the band concert next week."

Emily was even more upset when she and Ben came back later in the day with the tickets, which he handed to Blanche. As he took Emily's arm and steered her down the central hall to his little dark library, they heard Louise in the parlor saying, "I hope these are better seats than he got us last time."

Ben pulled a wry face as he closed the library door. It was clear he knew nothing he did would ever give satisfaction. Emily's heart was swelling with indignation for him even as he said, shamefacedly, "You mustn't blame her. I can see how I've been a disappointment to her. I don't care about any of the places she likes to go, nor about society, nor making a show. I'm just an aggravating old stick-in-the-mud. You can understand that."

She shook her head at him, trying to smile.

"Well, no, *you* wouldn't." Giving her a quick hug, he smiled down at her in just his old loving way. She found herself blinking away a mist before her eyes. *Dear* Ben!

Later, Emily heard Louise scolding because Ben would not promise to go to Maine with her and the children for the summer.

Chewing anxiously on his lip, he later explained to Emily, "I'll escort them up and see them settled in. Much as I'd like to stay, the mill won't run itself. And besides, we need the money."

Emily tried to hide her vexation for him, but thought resentfully that it was going to be hard enough for Ben to toil all summer in the heat, and come home evenings to an echoing house, without Louise making him feel guilty about it.

Evening Primrose: "Change"

1878

May 24, 1878: More papers from CWF. Strange he does not forget me.

This time, the colonel had circled a decision by the Supreme Court:

Man is and should be woman's protector. The domestic sphere is the proper one for women. This is the law of the Creator.

"The law of the Creator, indeed! Hannah, there is absolutely no talking to that man," she declared.

July 17, 1878: Went to Rochester to a Suffrage Meeting. Mrs. Stanton presided, Susan B. Anthony everywhere. Lucretia Mott there.

In exchanging warm greetings with Mrs. Mott, Emily apologized, "I do not belong here in this thirtieth anniversary celebration. Thee will remember I was forbidden to go to thy first meeting in Seneca Falls."

Susan B. Anthony, who was passing behind Emily, stopped with a jerk and exclaimed, drolly, "Well, in that case, neither do I belong here. *I* scoffed at Sister Mary's enthusiasm when she came home from the meeting."

They all smiled, but Lucretia spoke firmly, "Well, however you came into the fold, you both belong here. We could not do without you. So many are gone now, new hands must do the work."

Aug 18, 1878: Sojourner Truth spoke at Friends' Meeting. Witty and original. You's all a-dreaming.

Aug 20, 1878: Sojourner Truth and Mrs. Titus came from John Searings' before I had any work done.

Sojourner had said upon arrival, "Has you got yesterday's paper, 'cause I's anxious to hear what's the news." Emily had read out the headlines for her attentive guest, as well as an article she had particularly asked to hear. Sojourner then went on to remark, "Well, I's glad that meeting in Rochester stirred us up. If we once lets the woman question quiet down, it'll take a great while to get it stirring again."

She looked from Emily to Mrs. Titus with her wise old eyes. "I's been forty years a slave and forty years free, and I guess I's got to wait forty years more to see women get their rights same as men."

Aug 21, 1878: Mrs. Titus & I had a good talk together. Sojourner went to G. Weaver's for the day.

Aug 22, 1878: In p.m. took Sojourner down to Mosher Hall to hold her women's meeting.

I dreaded it because only her earnestness and age redeem her efforts from coarseness and vulgarity. A goodly number were present and she seemed to make an impression. I came home relieved.

Emily had been aghast when, after her speech, Sojourner declared right in the meeting that she must go out for a smoke. Would they be affronted? Fortunately, the women were disarmed and even amused by Sojourner's good-natured explanation, "I's been sent back to the smoking car so often, I's got to smoking in self-defense. I'd rather swallow my own smoke than somebody else's."

Anxious though she might have been about Sojourner's outspokenness, Emily felt the magnetism of this great-hearted woman. Sojourner, rising above her cruel abuse as a slave, testified so strongly in her great, deep voice and sang her "homemade songs" so movingly that she swept her audience to indignation at injustice, to laughter, or to worship.

Especially was Emily struck by Sojourner's impassioned cry that Negroes were not yet free, that a law alone did not bring true freedom. Briefly, Emily also doubted whether true freedom for women could ever come, even if they were granted the ballot someday. Then she caught herself up quickly. Women must press on. The law was the first step.

More than ever, she felt this when Isabel brought home an engaging young friend, a junior at Cornell, whom Emily had met before on campus. Isabel now announced, airily, "It was this same

Harriet May Mills who taught me to act like a scullery maid around their lordships." And both girls giggled.

Harriet May added with satisfaction, "And doesn't it make them mad when the scullery maids lead the class in marks!" She grinned all over her bright, eager, open face.

Emily exclaimed, "Ezra Cornell wanted women to attend his college as equals."

"Never mind, Aunt Emily. We are getting what we want," soothed Isabel.

Harriet May's face set in resolute lines. "Yes, we may cringe and shrink now, and dress to look like mice and then tolerate being sneered at as frumps and dowdies. But when I leave with a degree equal to any of theirs, I shall do my utmost to change this attitude."

Isabel put in, "Hattie May will, too. That runs in her family."

Emily was following her own train of thought. "Thee is from Syracuse. I knew a Samuel May there who headed the Syracuse Freedman's Relief Association, from which I sometimes received funds during the war. He was also a most moving Abolitionist speaker."

Harriet May smiled delightedly, "Yes, I was named for him. In fact, my folks moved to Syracuse because of Dr. May and his work in the Underground Railroad. It wasn't 'til long after that Father thought it was safe to talk of all their exciting doings, their rescues and their near-disasters."

Emily complained, "My menfolk would never open their mouths about their rescue work. I only learned of it by accident." Then frowning, she added, "I resented it then, and I believe I still do."

Harriet May said warmly, "I don't blame you. Hearing all those tales of high courage in dangerous doings has made me want to work for the underdog." At her friend's bubbling little laugh, she enquired, smiling, "Now what's the matter with you, Belle?"

"*We* are the underdogs, Hattie May!"

Harriet laughed also, but almost immediately turned back to Emily. "Did anyone ever tell you that just hours before Dr. May died, his friend, President White of Cornell, came to tell him that women students were to be admitted?"

Emily exclaimed, "I never knew that was one of Dr. May's concerns."

"It was one of his dearest wishes."

Isabel smiled affectionately at her aunt. "The two of you would have agreed perfectly about that, would you not?"

"We had many points of agreement," Emily nodded. "He was one of the few famous men who never faltered in his support of women's rights."

Harriet May said vigorously, "I am still angry about his funeral."

Her companions looked at her in surprise.

"One of his very first sermons upon coming to Syracuse way back in the '40s was on woman's rights. During all his twenty-five years here he spoke up for the women's side. But all that was conveniently forgotten at his funeral. Not one clergyman mentioned it, and not one woman was invited to speak."

As Emily went on answering Harriet May's questions about the leaders in the suffrage work, their meetings and their carrying of petitions, her heart rose at the girls' enthusiasm. One could trust the future to lively, bright young women like these.

Sept 20, 1878: Slocum Howland 84 today. Wrote Woman's Journal a reply to an article on the future of English women. Always feel better when I have given out an idea.

Jan 13, 1879: On reading Thomas Paine's Age of Reason, I think if he had written in less of the anger the other clergy showed toward him, his unanswerable arguments would have been more effective.

Putting down her pen, she sat looking at what she had written, but actually seeing again the scene at Miss Putnam's supper table. When she lost her temper, she had lost, for all time, the colonel's belief in her sincerity.

Jan 22, 1879: Went to Temperance Meeting again.

Jan 24, 1879: Sewing Society. Political Economy. I find nothing yet that I had not thought out.

Mar 4, 1879: Attended the debate. I felt conscious of speaking better than usual.

Mar 23, 1879: Took some Woman's Journals to Meeting for distribution. I see that I can do a good deal by giving out reading matter.

Mar 26, 1879: Had a 4 weeks wash done today. I strive, as Uncle Moses used to say, but I do not achieve much.

Apr 25, 1879: Down in the mouth. When one tries to do right, why suffer so much for what seem mistakes now. They may not be at all.

Soon Emily was uneasily reading that Frances Willard was link-

ing her temperance cause to the vote for women. Emily had heard
Colonel Folsom say he enjoyed his glass of wine at dinner. How ex-
asperated he must be!

> *July 2, 1879: Paper from CWF. I suppose we shall
> exchange no more letters.*

The colonel had, this time, circled an item on the stupidity of
linking two causes. "If women had gotten their way in 1864, they
would have scuttled suffrage for Negro males by tacking on their
ridiculous woman's rider."

> *July 4, 1879: A boat race advertised. It proved a horrible
> time...drunkenness, fights and a full lock-up at Ensenore.
> It was a disgrace to the town of Scipio.*

> *Aug 2, 1879: PicNic at Cascade. A steam yacht was the
> new feature of the occasion.*

> *Aug 12, 1879: Drawing class started at my house, with
> Mr. Santa, the artist.*

> *Sept 16, 1879: H. Phillips called. Told me what was
> pleasant to hear, that I had done her good. If I have made
> any human being somewhat more, I am content.*

As Emily greeted Harriet Phillips, she remembered that this same
Harriet was the infant who had travelled from Maryland in a bag
on the back of her father, Hermon Phillips, the fugitive slave.

This woman had been one of the party which traveled those hundreds of miles on foot, hiding in the woods by day and sighting by
the North Star at night. And Harriet had probably been the chief
danger to their expedition. How had they kept her from crying?

But now Emily must pay attention, for Harriet was anxiously
sitting forward in her chair. Clasping her workworn hands together
tightly, she resolutely began, "It's about grave markers for Pap and
Marm, Miss Emily. I've saved the money from my working out, but
I don't know how to get them."

"Yes, of course," responded Emily warmly. "Thy parents were good,
brave people and they should not be forgotten. If thee tells me how
thee wants their names and dates, I will write the order for thee,
here and now."

As they got up from the table with the order ready to send, it
came to Emily, "My father always said of the two of them, 'They
know how to work!' And that was high praise from him."

Harriet turned back from the door to say, "My Pap always said,
'That Slocum Howland is a saint!' He never forgot that Mr. Howland
bought his freedom."

Emily sat on afterward, savoring the warm satisfaction Harriet's visit had given her. Could she, by putting in a word in some cases or giving a hand in others, do a positive work right here, far from the Senate Chamber or speaker's platform?

Oct 13, 1879: Cambridge paper from CWF. Nothing but scoffing at W. Suffrage.

Nov 20, 1879: My birthday again. It is no use to repine over anything now or summon the "might have beens" but step right along as well and bravely as I can.

Dec 5, 1879: Read report of Boston schools sent by CWF.

The colonel also wrote her this winter of rereading some of the letters he had collected from prominent New Englanders through the years, especially while he was secretary of Harvard's Phi Beta Kappa Society. She could hardly imagine such a collection as included letters from John Quincy Adams, Ralph Waldo Emerson, Oliver Wendell Holmes, Henry Wadsworth Longfellow, Daniel Webster, and so many other great scholars and statesmen.

She, too, had some precious letters, though not hundreds, as he had.

Mar 6, 1880: I think I will collect some letters I have from distinguished persons. I believe all my relations with that kind of people must be at an end. The war gave us a grand shaking up.

Apr 1, 1880: Friend Theo. and I have much talk. I wish she had a chance to expand.

She is smothered under her bro.'s bigotry and does not dare to be what she was made to be. She is so limited her mind is frittered away. I fear she will marry uncongenially to escape.

Apr 12, 1880: To Mrs. Coffin's where I had a pleasant chat until the hack came to take me to So. Auburn. The r.r. cars moved away a little past 5. I could have got a good rest but for my stays.

Apr 14, 1880: In Philadelphia. Met Cornelia Hancock. To a meeting of Associated Charity in which Cornelia is interested.

Apr 29, 1880: I went to Mary Robinson's. Miss M. bade me to remember my dreams, as I had never slept in the house. Strange to say, I dreamed of seeing Colonel Folsom whom probably I never shall meet again. He is so associ-

ated with Virginia, I suppose the prospective trip bro't him to dreamland.

Apr 30, 1880: On Chesapeake Bay. Going back to old scenes one finds one's measure of growth. I feel that I am less self-conscious.

May 1, 1880: Chambermaid told me we should land at Port of Coan at 6 a.m. Instead she called me 20 minutes before 5, saying they would stop but a moment. I had to leave the boat with shoes unbuttoned and dress, hair uncombed and left my parasol and breast pin. I rode up with Mr. Rice to Heathsville. I am to pay him $.70 for the ride. I sit by the open fire, the air is cool. Apples are set. The place looks improving.

Putting aside her journal and stretching out her toes to the low fire, she reflected that she never had come South without the smiles of her friends here at Arcadia telling her that her experiment was successful. Though they might suffer setbacks in lean years or meet with snubs from white neighbors, one look at Ella's serene face always reassured her.

She looked around now at a sudden shushing sound from one of the teachers. "Thee does not need to quiet the children for me," she said quickly. "Let them do just as they usually do." She smiled invitingly at the young boarders who were peeping curiously around the door frame at her.

Some were shy and entered hesitantly. Two, bolder than the others, knelt before the fire, looking up at her with friendly grins.

Having all these students flocking in from far enough that they needed to board in the house was heartening. To Emily, it proved that teaching domestic and trade skills, as well as the three R's, was filling an urgent need.

A young girl sidled close and murmured, "My dress came out of the barrel."

Just as quietly, Emily answered, "There's no shame to that. It's a nice dress." Then looking closer, she turned the hem over. As she had thought, the color was much brighter inside. Beckoning the girl closer, she said softly, "Ask thy sewing teacher to help thee pick out the seams, so thee can sew it together the other side out. Then it will be all refreshed." She gave the girl a conspiratorial nod and smile.

When she later visited the shop in the new annex, she noted that only the boys were learning to mend shoes. She immediately asked, "Why aren't the girls in this class, too?" When the teacher looked surprised, she went on, "After all, if the mothers know how, the children will not go barefooted. Even if fathers cobble shoes for a living, we can't be sure their own children will benefit."

Far from minding, Emily enjoyed sharing quarters. On this visit, with both teachers and students boarding in her house, every hour offered new interests.

This break from home duties was soon followed by another, completely different but equally delightful:

> *July 26, 1880: Came to Boston to attend Concord*
> *School of Philosophy (through August 14th.) Miss*
> *Peabody here. Mrs. Emerson, Mr. Bronson Alcott, a tall*
> *grand-looking old man. Mr. Ralph Waldo Emerson looks*
> *a good deal impaired mentally. Very sad. Mr. Alcott and*
> *Miss Peabody speak often.*

How cozy and cheery the Alcott home was, with crimson chairs and lounges, and the wealth of books, pictures and flowers artistically arranged.

At the heart of it all was Bronson Alcott with his silver halo and gentle cultured tones, never speaking an ungenerous word.

Emily was delighted to greet Elizabeth Peabody, in her sadly draggled gown, with her hair tumbling about her face as usual. This eccentric but charming woman had introduced the German idea of kindergarten by opening her own in Boston in 1861. To Emily, she seemed like a young child herself, in her innocence and sweetness. How oddly her general air of incompetence sat on such a well-known lecturer.

"Emily Howland," cried Miss Peabody. "I do not believe we have met since we went together to that reception at the White House.

Emily chuckled, "I remember thee showing President Lincoln that leaflet with such a scathing criticism of him."

Miss Peabody also smiled. "Oh, wasn't it a wicked thing? I will never forget his saying, 'Oh yes, I've seen it. I like it.' He was a noble man."

Then they hurried off to Miss Peabody's lecture. Later, however, Emily enquired after Mr. Alcott's daughter, Louisa May, who was away from home at present.

"She has never fully regained her health after taking the typhoid while she was nursing the soldiers in the Great War. And she has had so much sorrow, losing two sisters and her mother. Still, she is brave, and keeps on with her writing."

Yet later, in a quiet chat, Elizabeth shared an incident she had heard from Louisa Alcott, which much impressed Emily:

"When Louisa and her mother were watching at her sister Beth's deathbed, a few moments after the last breath came, each of them saw a light mist rise from the body and float up and vanish in the air. The doctor said it was the life departing visibly."

This story was to be a comfort to Emily during her losses of the next two years, reinforcing her firm conviction that the soul lives on.

When Isabel graduated from Cornell University in 1881, Emily felt a deep fulfillment at her accomplished young relative receiving the degree which she herself had longed to earn.

After the ceremony, she greeted the girl, "Isabel, I'm proud thee has won through!"

Isabel, surprised, asked, "Why ever do you say it that way?"

"I've been anxious whether thee could do well under such difficulties."

Isabel gave her hand a warm squeeze. "Dear Aunt, I wish I had known thee was worried. There were little drawbacks, but I never thought of it as difficult. It was fun!"

As a fellow graduate touched her arm, she turned aside, with a word of apology. Emily's eyes followed her with love and pride. She need not worry about this girl. Belle was strong and able for anything. Emily's heart rejoiced, as well, at the girl's deliberate use of "thee." To Emily, this spoke volumes of affection, for Belle had dropped the old pronouns while in college, except in tender or emotional moments such as this glad day.

This joy was soon quenched, for, in June, Emily's father, Slocum Howland, died. At first she felt she had lost the focus of her life: the ordering of his home and his meals and his comfort and amusement. Later she wrote in her diary:

> *I felt grieved for him, restless, and that he was so used to this life and comfortable in it that it must be hard for him to have to leave it. I had a feeling I could not reason down that he was homesick there.*

Emily's father had been her sounding board, her partner and her steady support. It was with him she had shared her new idea, to build a larger school for Hepsibeth Hussey here in Sherwood. His warm approval had encouraged her. He had treated her as an equal always. Well, except once, when he took her out of school in Philadelphia, and surely he could be forgiven for giving in to Mother on just that one occasion.

Now, with him gone, she had come to a crossroads. Keeping his home, entertaining his company, and seeing to his welfare no longer tied her to Sherwood. She was a wealthy woman now, and independent. Would she join her many friends in crusading for woman's rights?

The rest of the year went by and she did not take up the active work she had craved to do. Was she emotionally spent? Was planning a larger school building here in Sherwood occupying her mind and energies? Or was she self-conscious about what the colonel would have to say?

She did tell Hannah, "He always focuses on immoderation and absurdities. He has never ceased to gibe at me about the Bloomer girls, after thirty years, or that 'Saloon Woman' as he insists on calling Frances Willard, who is such a proper lady. And it does seem that only immoderation catches attention and pokes up the public conscience. But I do wish ridicule were not such an effective weapon against progress."

In 1881, President Garfield rebuffed Frances Willard at the White House, and still Emily received no editorial from the colonel. She found herself watching the mail and missing his usual challenge.

However, she had plenty to do in sorting and clearing out Father's things. Among his papers, she found a letter, a single sheet much worn and darkened by age and handling, which folded to form its own envelope, and which was addressed:

Slocum Howland
Sherwood's Corners
Scipio N.Y.
Owego
Ithica [sic]

Opening it, she read with awe:

I have mailed two passengers to thee, in the "shank's horse diligence": baggage free, and at the risk of the owners.

9th of 4th month 1840 John Mann

and below, in Father's hand, the explanation:

This note introduced two fugitives from Slavery in Maryland, Thomas and James Hart, stalwart vigorous and young.

One might call this a ticket on the Underground Railroad, she supposed. It was a passport to safety for two poor fellows.

At first, the "ticket" intrigued her as a clue to the mysterious workings of the Underground Railroad. Then, upon envisioning the fugitives' escape with the owner or his agent in hot pursuit, and their being handed these directions at their last stop before Father's, she suddenly shivered. What if they had been caught and this paper taken from them? It would have named two stationmasters, leading to reprisals and making their stops worthless. How dangerous, how foolhardy, to write names and addresses!

Mar 14, 1882: Invited to young Mr. Wm. Seward's to the Historical Society.

Ah, what a treat this offered! How this visit would take her back, to many happy hours with her own Mrs. Seward and, of course, Fanny. What a good friend she had possessed in Frances Seward. Oh, much more than friend: confidante, counsellor, patron saint.

Mar 16, 1882: I was delighted to go to the house of precious memories. It is much more stately and elegant than of old. William and Mrs. Seward welcomed me most graciously. The paper was reminiscences of Auburn from its beginning. Then Dr. Hawley asked young Mr. Seward to explain the crimson banner presented to his father by a Mandarin.

The face embroidered in the center was his father, Mr. Seward; across the top were the three sons. William the youngest was holding his baby son. The artist being told William had children, "a boy and a girl," brought the rejoinder, "don't want the girls." When Secretary Seward said he had three sons and 2 daughters, "We do not want the daughters." It seems amazing that a nation could so long exist that had such a contempt for its women.

Choice refreshment followed, then we wandered through the old house. Young Mrs. Seward showed me all thru into the old tower where I've held sweet converse with Mrs. Frances Seward. Mrs. Seward deserved the blessing of good sons, and they do bear witness to her care and love.

Mar 17, 1882: Attended Peace Meeting. I was made Corresponding Secy. I have repented since for I have too much to do of that kind.

Apr 5, 1882: Talked thru the telephone for the first time.

Even before Emily's father died, Hepsibeth's school had become overcrowded, and Emily's imagination had caught fire. Now, out of the $100,000 Father had left her, here was one service she could offer this community.

Apr 14, 1882: I went to see Hepsibeth C. Hussey to talk over the school house that is to be.

That same month, William brought Emily the news that her brother, Benjamin, had died of an accidental blow on the head from a falling timber in his Catskill mill. Emily was pierced to the heart. Ben, whom she had so often comforted, and who had comforted her; who had written her of his first homesick days at Haverford College; who had supported her when she wished to teach in Washington. Always Ben had been one of her warmest and most faithful friends, writing regularly when they could not meet. Oh, how she would miss those letters! How could she do without him?

Apr 26, 1882: I thought when Father went, nothing could so smite me again, but my darling brother!

Yet, life must go on, and she would not be turned aside from her purpose. On that same desolate day, she wrote resolutely:

Apr 26, 1882: H. C. Hussey came. We went over the ground and decided on the school location farther south.

May 8, 1882: Dear Ben! If I miss him more than anyone else, it is because he was more to me. He had mental resources which were always a comfort, his love of the beautiful, too, and his generous spirit. Not for worlds would I bid him back. I feel as though his release must be such a joy to him.

May 14, 1882: William and I went down to the school house grounds and put stakes for the house.

To William, she confided how pleased she was that the school was adjoining her home property. It would be just a pleasant little step away.

May 14, 1882: Would I take Benj. from a happy existence in a congenial sphere, to live with one who only knew how to make home unpleasant?

When I think how sadness grew upon his face, like President Lincoln's. There is no gloom ever written on the face as that which is limned by unhappy homes. How hard every part of that wretched marriage has been to the poor dear.

Those for whom he slaved leave him with brief regrets. One daughter has written of going to Lynn, having a lovely time in the gaiety of society.

May 24, 1882: Wm. Gardner & his assistants began to dig the cellar for the new school house.

It was a busy a.m. so I did not take up the first shovel full. It is truly a work full of beneficent meaning for the future to have a school of high character permanently established here in Sherwood.

June 13, 1882: I saw Harriet Tubman. My dress cost so much that I had nothing to buy curtain rods. I paid $21.50 for making & trimmings, making the whole dress $34. I had one made in Philadelphia, nice in every way, cost $21.16. I have decided to cease entirely from this extravagance.

July 26, 1882: Walked down to the school. The timbers are laid on the foundations.

Aug 30, 1882: A circus in Auburn. A neighbor deplored shows but went to Auburn and saw the parade. Easy for people who can take long journeys to decry the amusements of those who cannot.

Sept 28, 1882: The tinners eat dinner here and the work goes slowly on—to my impatience scarcely perceptible.

Oct 5, 1882: Sent Conrad to Seneca Falls for weather vane and bell. He returned this evening without the vane but got a bell.

Emily chuckled as she wrote, for the arrival of the bell had caused much excitement in Sherwood. A small lad had hopped on the wagon for a ride and had rung the bell from one end of the village to the other, with people hanging out of windows or popping out of doors.

Oct 7, 1882: Peace meeting in the little hall at Ledyard. Good audience.

After the meeting, a woman remarked, "I do not see why you concern yourself with building that schoolhouse. What will you ever get out of it?"

"A great deal of satisfaction," Emily answered quickly, smiling.

"And I suppose you'll have a bunch of women teaching. What kind of a job is that for a woman?"

"Faithful teachers are the world's best benefactors," she declared stoutly. And with those words, she realized once again that teaching and setting up schools, despite her early bitter disappointment, had been the right answer for her.

Oct 9, 1882: Was ever a greater contrast in some regards in two brothers than in mine? I often think if Ben and I were neighbors how different our association would be.

Oct 23, 1882: A boisterous wind which worried me greatly, thinking of the roof of the new building. I could scarcely eat, my anxiety was so great, but stirring about in the fresh air restored the equilibrium.

Nov 14, 1882: Visit to Miss Withington at Sage Hall at Cornell, and attended lectures. I am glad young people do not seem to have any dread of me.

Except Herbert, she mentally added. Isabel's brother was a freshman at Cornell this fall, and seeing Emily on campus, he had turned a corner hastily to avoid having to acknowledge her before his friends. That arrogant young man!

Now his ego would be even more swollen, for his father had just been elected to the state assembly this month. For William's sake, though, she was glad. He had ability and integrity; now he would be of wider service, and better known.

Nov 7, 1882: Roof completed today. Joy! 7 weeks since they began!

Nov 18, 1882: Went to Poplar Ridge and ordered a new harness. I got the most costly, perhaps I ought not, but I liked the rubber covered buckles best and thought I did not often indulge in extravagances, if this be one. Now I write it, I think I will rescind my order.

Dec 10, 1882: Getting things together to send South. I used to think I might sometime cease from this work but I suppose not while life lasts.

Dec 20, 1882: Went to Auburn. Bought presents, spent $4.50 in articles from $.75 for the highest down to 1 cent. I bought Hawthorne's complete works for $10. I think it is a high price but I wanted Belle to have them for a Christmas gift.

Dec 31, 1882: The new school building is done! More than 3 cheers!

The Howland Chapel School at Heathville, Virginia, built in 1867. Restored in 1989 and enrolled in the Virginia Landmarks Register.

Emily Howland as she appeared in midlife.

The Sherwood Select School at Sherwood, New York, 1882–1954

Dog Rose: "Pleasure and Pain"

1883

The new building opened its doors for the January term, and Hepsibeth reported more than fifty-five students attending. Now that the bustle of finishing the building was over, Emily would have felt let down except that she was looking forward to the Suffrage Convention in Boston.

As she began to fold her clothes into her trunk, she could not help thinking wistfully of the colonel. What a strange and prickly friendship they had shared. Although he still lived in Boston, they had differed so bitterly of late years, she was sure he would not want to meet her now.

However, she looked forward to visiting with Lucy Stone who was bringing her prenuptial agreement. Emily marveled that, during almost thirty years of marriage and partnership in publishing their suffragist *Woman's Journal*, Henry Blackwell had treated Lucy as his equal.

> *Feb 12, 1883: At Boston. Met Lucy Stone, Miss Peabody. Attended lectures.*

Emily read Lucy's prenuptial agreement with deep interest, savoring aloud the points that especially struck her:

> *Laws of marriage...confer upon the husband an injurious superiority...which no man should possess. We protest against laws which give to the husband the custody of the wife's person...the exclusive control of their children...the sole ownership of her estate. Personal independence and equal rights can never be forfeited.*

Looking up, Emily asked, "Lucy, who wrote this?"

Lucy laughed delightedly. "We both wrote it, of course!"

Emily sat looking at it and finally she sighed. "Thy Henry must be a remarkable man. I know of no other male who would write and sign such a statement."

Feb 14, 1883: C. W. Folsom here. Was so surprised. More than 14 years since we parted.

At her exclamation, the colonel's eyes had lighted with amusement in just the old way. "Now Emily! I made a point of seeing the list of delegates. You cannot imagine I'd let the little carpetbagger come to Boston without my seeing her?"

Oh, how that took her back. There was no time for remembering, though, for of course he must inquire about their Arcadian project, and how her colored families were faring. And they must exchange news of mutual friends. Then their talk had to give way to the general conversation. Still, their eyes returned to each other often, searching for samenesses and changes.

Feb 16, 1883: CWF came for supper. We had a sociable evening.

Emily had been a bit uneasy when the colonel met Lucy Stone this second evening. As he came in the entry, he had hissed, "Is that the woman who refuses to use her husband's name?"

Emily watched anxiously. Though his eyes did not warm when they fell upon Lucy, he was perfectly pleasant and courteous.

Feb 22, 1883: CWF came and spent the evening.

Tonight they could draw a little apart from the others, to chat on politics and the trends of the modern world. Somehow they found themselves talking of the temperance movement.

Emily explained her stand, proudly, "Father tolerated no liquor in his store. Other storekeepers gave free liquor to customers but Father always kept a pitcher of water on the counter."

"Emily, I do not believe you understand the difference between the hard liquor which ruins the working man's home and the moderate glass of wine served on a gentleman's table. If you could see me when I have had a glass of wine...."

She interrupted, breathlessly, "Oh dear, I should not like *that*."

He chuckled. "Well, it is not so very bad, I assure you. I am not in the least inebriated, just a bit at ease."

"Oh, I do not like to hear about it," she exclaimed, much worried. "Must thee do so?"

He shook his head smiling. "I cannot make you understand it, can I?"

Feb 24, 1883: Mrs. Stone and I visited the
Frothinghams at Milton. I always wish I knew more when
with highly cultured people, indeed my wish is not con-
fined to these occasions, but the lack is more painful then.

Feb 25, 1883: CWF came and we had a pleasant p.m.
He staid to tea and afterward we went to Boston Museum.
Long talk with CWF.

"If you had accepted my suit," he said at length, "on such a Sunday afternoon as this, we would be sitting in Mother's parlor, and perhaps you would be reading to her."

She countered, smiling, "Might thee not be reading to me?" Taken by surprise, he protested, "No, no, we have to think of Mother." Then he reluctantly laughed, and half in exasperation, exclaimed, "You never stop fighting, do you? If you'd been a man, you'd have been a senator by now!"

Then, his face clearing, he went on, "You've never met Mother, of course...nor my sister. And she did invite us for supper. Will you come?"

Emily was more than a little curious to meet his mother, who commanded such devotion. She did say, thinking to spare his purse, "Thou need not take a hack for me. I should enjoy riding one of those horse-drawn streetcars."

"No, no, they're too slow. It's four miles, over the river and into Cambridge."

From the proud tilt of his head, she knew he was insisting because a gentleman liked to offer only his best to a special lady. Hugging this thought, she enjoyed the ride all the more.

"I always let myself in on Sundays, since the maid is out," he said as he ushered Emily up the steps of the imposing Bixby Street house. In the dark chilly hall, he dropped his hat on the hall table.

His sister Mary, a well-dressed but colorless female, hovered in the archway to the parlor. Offering Emily a cold limp hand, she gasped, "How do you do," in a trembling voice. However, if she was alarmed by the woman her brother had brought home, her mother was not.

Nor was this erect, handsome lady sitting by the modest fire cordial, though to the colonel's introductory remark, "Miss Howland is attending that women's meeting over in Boston," she replied politely, "Is that so?"

Emily took a seat near the matron and offered pleasantly, "We have several interesting personages as speakers."

Mrs. Folsom repeated, "Is that so?" and looked as wonderingly at Emily as she might survey a strange beast at the menagerie.

With an effort, Emily refrained from straightening her hat. Half annoyed and half amused, she asked herself what this woman had expected a suffragist to look like.

Before the colonel could take a hand in the conversation, Miss Mary Folsom was quick to prompt, "Charles, Mother thinks that clock on the mantel is running a little slow."

The colonel grunted impatiently under his breath, but obediently went to the mantel and opened the clock, the eyes of both his relatives upon him.

Emily, feeling ignored and unwanted, sank back and let her eyes wander. She did not admire the dark heavy hangings, the fashionable clutter of small velvet chairs and marble-topped tables crowded with ornately framed likenesses. How stifling it all was.

Miss Folsom, looking over the colonel's shoulder as he worked, suddenly asked, "Charles, for our Literary Club meeting, I need to know where it is the Statue of Liberty is going to stand."

Absently, he answered, "The Boston Harbor," and opening his pocket knife, began a careful adjustment.

Emily, startled, had her mouth open to correct him, when she caught a curious look passing between the two women, and especially Mrs. Folsom's tiny shake of the head at her daughter. Then the older woman flowed smoothly on, "Charles, Cook has asked for Wednesday to go to the wedding of her niece. Do you think we should permit her to do that?"

Without looking up from his tinkering, the colonel answered firmly, "Why, I think you must let her go to her niece's wedding."

"It is not quite convenient for us, you know, Charles."

"She is entitled to that consideration after the years she's been with you," he insisted.

"I suppose you are right, dear," she conceded. "And then also, we talked about the carpet for the spare bedroom."

With perfect patience, he inquired, "Do you want me to go with you to pick it out?"

"Oh, yes, I should be so glad if you will," and she sighed with relief.

"Now Mother, I think this clock is right back where it was when you said it was a trifle fast. It's my belief there's no adjustment in between. But we'll try it and see how it goes." And closing its back, he straightened it on the mantel and came back to sit down.

With a fond smile at her son, Mrs. Folsom said, "I do not know what we would do without you, Charles."

The colonel laughed and pointed out to Emily the small picture on the table at her elbow. "Yes, Mother has always called me her little man, haven't you, Mother?"

Emily had noticed this painted miniature of the colonel as a small boy, and now felt free to look at it more closely. Even then he had a stubborn chin, she thought. How oddly this accorded with his saying easily, "Mother needs me, don't you?"

"You are very good to us, indeed, Charles." Mrs. Folsom turned to Emily with another of her very direct looks. "Charles comes every Sunday afternoon and every Wednesday evening, and he always reads to us. With this one exception, of course."

The colonel said quickly, "But I'm here this evening instead, Mother. Shall I read now?"

"Oh no, I am sure you would rather not," she said, wistfully.

Emily looked at her in surprise. This woman was forthright with her, yet how different was her manner with her son.

"I'm quite willing, Mother," he insisted, reaching for the book on the center table. "We are at chapter eight, are we not?"

"Well," conceded Mrs. Folsom meekly, "if *you* think we should."

So! Emily eyed her thoughtfully. This was a rather clever lady.

As the colonel took up the story, Emily realized that not only did he have a deep and moving voice but he was reading with exceptional expression. Smiling with pleasure, she turned to Mrs. Folsom, whose attention was all on her son. Miss Folsom, on the other hand, was hastily withdrawing her sideways gaze. Oh, well! Leaning back her head, Emily closed her eyes and gave herself up to the delight of simply listening as he unfolded the story.

By the time he finished the chapter and laid the book aside, Emily had told herself firmly that one must be fair. Mrs. Folsom was not being intentionally rude; her searching looks were natural for someone who believed that any feminist had to be radical and odd.

Mrs. Folsom now asked Charles to go to the kitchen with her to carry in the tea tray. The moment they were out of earshot, Miss Folsom said, in a trembling voice, her eyes still not quite meeting Emily's, "There, you see how she depends on him."

In a flash of insight, Emily saw the woman's desperate fear. Of course! For if her mother should die, and if her brother had cast her off in favor of a wife, what would become of this poor woman?

Leaning toward Miss Folsom, Emily reassured her warmly, "Thee need not be anxious about me. The colonel and I are just friends."

Her voice still trembling and her gaze still sliding away, Miss Folsom declared jealously, "I rather think *we* know Charles too well to require any such assurance."

All thoughts of fairness flew out of Emily's head. How much she longed to blurt, "Well think again, thou old silly! He *did* ask me, so there!" But then she swallowed her wrath, for what difference did it make? She would never see this pathetic creature again.

Nevertheless, it did most regrettably please her that the colonel was handing about little cakes which were dry and nearly as tasteless as the pale tea. What a meal for these two to offer a man! No wonder he kept bachelor's quarters.

As soon as she and the colonel left the house, after an exchange of seemingly cordial farewells, he asked complacently, "Well, what did you think of them?"

"Why...they seem very ladylike and courteous." Emily could think of nothing more.

Luckily, this satisfied him. "Yes, they're very feminine, aren't they? They save all their little problems and questions for me." He smiled reminiscently, then suddenly jerked to a halt. "Thunderation! *Where* did I tell them the Statue of Liberty is to be?"

She burst out laughing at his consternation. "Never mind, we all knew thee misspoke!"

"Why didn't *you* say something?"

"I didn't quite like to..."

After a puzzled look at her, he said quite seriously. "Well, I must remember to tell them. I certainly do not wish to mislead them."

Just as if they could not think for themselves, she thought.

As they again walked on toward the hack stand, he confided, "It's been a sacrifice to stay in Boston since the war. There have been so many excellent opportunities in young, developing cities for engineers with my experience. But as you saw, I could never have left them."

She looked up at him searchingly. How strange that this masterful man imagined he was in charge of that household, while his mother managed him with hints and sighs and smiles. Was this the womanly behavior he had looked for from her?

It would be futile to say anything. And after all, it was taking nothing away from Emily.

Mar 1, 1883: CWF got my ticket. He met me at the station, sat by me until the train was ready to leave. It was a new experience to be so cared for.

Each of them knew these were likely the last moments they would ever spend together. There were questions they must ask, now.

"Aren't you sometimes lonely, Emily?"

"Yes," she admitted honestly. Looking back, though, she saw that she had thrived better singly. She had become a person she could never have been with him, but there was no use saying that to him.

"I was wounded when you refused me. I never could see any reason for it," he complained sadly.

She looked at him fondly, smiling and shaking her head. The same hopelessly blind and yet sweet colonel! It was too pleasant sitting with him to bother about rights and wrongs today. She said mildly, "Perhaps it was unfortunate that we met. There must have been any number of congenial females, any of whom could have made thee comfortable."

He shook his head and his eyes were so tender, she did not trust her voice. They sat on, side by side, silent until her train was called.

Mar 2, 1883: Back in Syracuse. Went to Dr. Sanford's. I told her my secret. She was very glad for me without any reservations.

What a pleasure it had been to share with this trusted friend and protégé that the stout bond between the two of them was still unbroken... that neither of them had ever forgotten... that the colonel still cared for her.

She sat on, gazing at what she had just written in her diary, but seeing those warm, dark eyes smiling down into hers.

Mar 11, 1883: Wrote CWF a long letter.

Mar 29, 1883: I wrote a long letter on W. Suffrage (there were 7 sheets.)

She weighed the envelope in her hand. Never minding what the postage would cost, she had written him a rational explanation of her views of why women should have the vote. Not one speck of emotion, either of pleading or anger, had she allowed to creep in. Would he finally give her a fair reading?

A month later, when the mail arrived, her spirits bounded as she recognized the writing on a heavy envelope. Tearing it open, she eagerly scanned the first page, and then, with compressed lips she sat down to read the same old arguments once more.

*Apr 25, 1883: Long letter from CWF. Not exhilarating
but profitable. I am seeing clearly that I must return to
active work for humanity. I need it; the work needs me.*

Emily had enjoyed Isabel's company this year, especially during
their painting lessons, at which Emily had started a set of tiles for
her fireplace. Though she and Isabel talked many hours as they
painted, they never came to the end of their pleasure in each other's
ideas.

Sometimes they laid plans for their trip south this spring. In the
end, it included visits to Baltimore, Washington, Richmond and
Cornelia's school at Charleston. It was particularly pleasant taking
Isabel to Arcadia, and showing off the Howland School which had
now grown to more than seventy-five students. They stayed two
nights with the teachers in Emily's house, and inspected the annex
Uncle Aleck Day had built, which housed the shops and part of the
boarders.

Both Emily and Belle then wanted to see Carrie Putnam at
Lottsburgh. While she was finishing her last class of the day, Sallie
Holley welcomed them and showed them about. Although Emily had,
several years ago, invited Sallie to speak in the Brick Meeting House
at Sherwood and had given her overnight lodging, she had still had
a lingering feeling that such a campaigner might be proud and overbearing on her own ground.

Sallie now proved to be gracious and pleasant, speaking of Carrie in a way that warmed Emily's heart, and never once referring to
her friend as "Putty."

"How pleasant this is," remarked Belle, looking about at the
freshly whitewashed and well-kept buildings and the flower borders, strawberry beds, melon patches, and grape arbors. "I should
like to visit in season to sample all these delights."

Emily said to Sallie, "I am more impressed by thy saying thee
will barter good garments from the barrels of clothes for chickens or
the promise of weeding, or other fair payment. I like thy rule that
'He who will not work can go without.'"

Sallie nodded decisively. "We must not make dependents of these
people."

Of the classroom work, Sallie later said, "Hundreds have learned
to read and write in this school, but not a single white among them.
It is appalling that the slave owners, in withholding schooling from
the blacks, have doomed most of the whites to ignorance as well."
She shook her head sadly. "The poor wretches! Too proud to let their

children come to learn in our 'colored' school. Is it not pitiful, their growing up without knowing 'a' from 'b'?"

After a good visit with Carrie Putnam, Emily and Isabel returned home by way of Catskill where Emily visited Benjamin's grave. How many happy hours they had shared. How close they had been, yet she could not wish him back. She could leave him here, satisfied that there was no more heartache for him.

June 2, 1883: 2 letters from CWF full of dislike for W. Suffrage.

She had written him wishing she had seen his great collection of letters from famous men, and he responded regretfully that he had finally thought of them while she was still in Boston, but too late to get them out of the bank for her to see.

June 9, 1883: Looked over CWF's letters.

Emily was interrupted at this bittersweet task by William, who wanted to go over accounts. After half an hour's concentrated checking and cross-checking, she threw down her pen and exclaimed, "Oh, William, what a heavy weight so much money seems."

July 12, 1883: I get only papers but am not disturbed. I know my friend's devotion to his mother.

July 22, 1883: Took my first French lesson.

Aug 5, 1883: Belle and I went to school and opened cases and began arranging apparatus. Cases put up. Minerals are in.

Herbert had lounged in, looking sleek and dapper, hands in pockets, and leaned against a laboratory table with a faintly scornful air. Finally, he muttered to Isabel, "I don't see why she gets so worked up about all this."

Emily, whose ears were excellent, was suddenly angry. "Thee has never worked. Thy father sends thee to the university with no effort whatever on thy part, yet thee takes for granted what others cannot have. And does thee appreciate thy advantages?"

"Oh, sorry, Aunt. Well, I must be going," he said, hastily edging toward the door.

She called after him, "These young people who have to work for their educations are the better for it. A little effort on thy part would do thee good."

Her only answer was the reverberation of the outside door closing. The two women looked at each other and then Emily said, ruefully, "Well, let us get back to work."

Aug 19, 1883: Wrote a long letter on W. Suffrage. I am tired of repeating myself to the same effect, to the same opponent.

In his June letter, the colonel declared that politics are dirty, that caucuses meet in saloons, and that women must not lower themselves to the mire as those *saloon women* do.

She responded tartly that they needed women such as the despised Frances Willard to clean them up.

He had commented, "I do not belittle women, for they are goddesses at their hearths, with special gifts, tender where men are strong."

To this, she replied, "That worn-out old argument was designed to keep women enslaved. Woman's work is important but not elevated, and no man really believes it is or he would be glad to do it."

She also wrote, "Thee refers to 'suffragettes who dance on the table.' What can thee mean? It is conceivable that a speaker might step up on a table for a platform to be heard over a crowd. But how can thee possibly confuse this with a saloon woman who dances on tables to entertain?"

As she folded the bulky letter into the envelope, she paused, feeling a moment's uneasiness. Was it possible, as the temperance movement had grown bolder with exposure in saloons, that some woman might have gone beyond the line of gentility?

Aug 23, 1883: Got to work among my pressed flowers and worked earnestly. I determined to group them in orders.

Sept 4, 1883: Night brought me a long scrawl on W. Suffrage. I am heartsick and now ready to say, 'Spare me, enough!' It must come. I have felt for 2 days that the time had come for the final word.

She again took up his letter: "Your last convinced me that women would vote with emotions, not with their reason. Women are all heart, easily swayed by any plausible scoundrel. Anyone can take advantage of them."

There was no possible rebuttal. To whatever she might write, he would say she was just being emotional. She took up her diary and pen again:

A contrast in my letters. One from Miss Chaplin telling that she was in love and it was reciprocated.

Sept 5, 1883: There is a mighty wrestling going on within.

Sept 16, 1883: Must give up correspondence with CWF?

Sept 30, 1883: I began a letter to CWF but could seem to think of nothing worth writing him so left it. If I could only see him once in a great while, I should be satisfied.

Oct 7, 1883: Letter from CWF. His self-sacrificing devotion to his mother is beyond anything I ever knew.

Now Emily felt her life to be suddenly pointless, with her school building done, and her re-awakened feelings toward the colonel still as bittersweet and prickly as ever. Isabel was teaching chemistry at the new school this fall, but Emily had no part in it except financially. She had an empty feeling as she watched Isabel hurrying by on her way to school of a morning. For who needed *her* now?

Oct 12, 1883: I work every p.m. on my herbarium. I have been collecting plants for more than 30 years and have long wanted to arrange them in orders.

Oct 17, 1883: Packed trunk for 11th Woman's Congress in Chicago.

During a recess period at the Congress, Emily paused to speak to Elizabeth Cady Stanton.

"Emily Howland!" exclaimed Elizabeth. "I never see you without remembering your letter at the time we fell out with Horace Greeley. Dear me!" And here she shook her head so all her white curls quivered and bounced around her smart carriage bonnet. "I resolved long ago never to mourn over my blunders... but neither Susan nor I saw how irrevocable a rupture with Horace would be. We knew he had already made up his mind against us even before the hearing, and it was just irresistible to pay him out. Stupid, stupid! If we had been perfect little ladies and taken our defeat without any fuss, he would have gone on printing our news in the *Tribune*, even if his editorials were against us. But after we riled him at that hearing, he never gave us another word."

Curiously, Emily asked, "Could thee have made it up with him?"

"We tried. Susan and I soon met him at a reception and put forth our friendliest smiles. He just snapped, 'You two ladies are the most maneuvering politicians in the state of New York,' and stalked off." Elizabeth shook her head sadly. "Horace was as stubborn as a billy goat, and yet he was the best friend we women ever had, and we had to spoil it!" Ruefully she added, "I think it was Henry Ward Beecher who said, 'Speak when you are angry and you'll make the best speech you'll ever regret.'"

During the next busy years, Emily heard nothing from the colonel. When she read of the WCTU convention in 1884 at St. Louis, she was confident of receiving a gibe about "That Saloon Woman" Frances Willard's inelegant call for an all-out national effort: "Temperance has failed at the local and state levels and will fail for so long as we save at the spigot and waste at the bung, to borrow an expression from the enemy."

Could he let that pass? Yet even with that provocation, no scathing letter or editorial ever arrived.

Swamp Magnolia: "Perseverance"

1884

In August of 1884, when Emily started on a sixteen-month tour of Europe, Belle was in her party for the first several months. Standing at the railing of the ship one morning, the girl remarked, "I am doing so little with my life compared to yours, Aunt Emily. I think of your plantation and your Howland School there. And then the support you give to other colored schools. I wonder if you even know how many?"

Emily smiled wryly, "Oh, yes, their solicitations continually remind me."

"A dozen at least, that I can name."

"Yes, and more," admitted Emily.

"And now you have built the Sherwood Select School to cap it all. But I'm without funds. What can I do, Aunt Emily?"

"So much needs doing! People urge me to carry more petitions and address more suffrage meetings, and hold more offices than one woman can possibly do. I should be very thankful for thy help."

Isabel turned a bright glance on her. "Oh, I should like very much to help in that work, Aunt Emily."

With Isabel as a partner, vigorous, able and so personable, what could they not achieve?

In the meantime, simply as a companion, she was delightful. Emily smiled at her enthusiasm for collecting pieces typifying the countries they visited.

"Won't our friends marvel at these lovely beads of real Venetian glass?" she exclaimed one day.

Though missing the girl sorely when she returned home in April, Emily went on with her tour. Her letters home were full of the delights and wonders she saw.

Isabel's, in return, brought all the Sherwood news. Once she wrote about Herbert's elation over the victorious season of the 1885 Cornell crew, on which he stroked. After another crew meet that fall, Herbert, her father and she chanced to meet retired President Andrew D. White of Cornell. She immediately fell back several steps to efface herself. Instead of congratulating Herbert, he asked her father, "Did you not also have a daughter who attended Cornell?" She had stepped forward then to speak with him. To her aunt, Belle wrote, "Herbert was annoyed." The thought of that conceited young man's discomfiture tickled Emily. She chuckled aloud over it later in the evening, to the surprise of the other women in her party.

Despite the pleasures of travel and the encouraging letters from home, she once wrote in her diary:

> *Sometimes I feel unworthy of having so much, and that I do not enough enjoy. I try to, but oh memory, haunting memory of the long past!*

Nevertheless, she came back refreshed from her long trip, to take up her round of home duties and causes and offices.

> *Sept 7, 1886: In Auburn went to see Katy Munhall about coming here to board and go to school.*

> *Sept 10, 1886: Katy came.*

> *Sept 13, 1886: School opened. 20 pupils. Better than I expected.*

Perhaps Emily's warmest satisfaction came when her eye fell upon Katy, sitting among the teachers around the dining table in the evening, her smooth head bent over her books. This bright young woman had opened the door to Emily at an Auburn doctor's office, where she attended the patients. Emily, always interested, had questioned her enough to learn how she hungered for an education, with no hope for help from her family. And now, here was Katy, aged twenty-four, but not too proud to sit here studying the lessons of the twelve-year-olds.

Emily could almost fancy it was her own younger self: an ardent young woman with a strong dream of practicing medicine. And however many years it might take, she, Emily was going to help this dream come true!

Katy, now and then, would suddenly raise her shining head and look around toward Emily with a warm smile, as though she never forgot to be grateful.

Emily was building a two-story addition on her house this year, with rooms for the Sherwood teachers who now boarded with her, and for her friends in the women's movement.

Susan B. Anthony, for one, lived out of a traveling bag on lecture tours. Fancying that she looked very worn one afternoon at a meeting in Auburn, Emily impulsively invited her to Sherwood to rest and be cosseted for a few days.

On the carriage ride out, Miss Anthony related with gusto some of the snags and the amusements she and Elizabeth Cady Stanton had met with, in sifting bushels of letters and references for their third volume of the *History of Woman Suffrage,* which they had just finished.

And then she vividly described seeing the dedication of the new Statue of Liberty that fall, from a steamer crammed with suffragists.

Emily said, wistfully, "I wish I could see that great scene through thine eyes."

Miss Anthony smiled broadly. "To be honest, we couldn't see it ourselves. Nor could our banners be seen. It was foggy, to begin with. And then there was so much smoke from all the cannon salutes, and so many vessels crowding about, we could hardly make out the statue herself. And from the moment President Garfield stepped onto Bedloe's Island, all the steamers whistled, and the cannon boomed practically throughout the ceremonies, so no one could hear a word."

"Well, I declare," chuckled Emily, "it sounds a rather dismal scene."

Miss Anthony laughed comfortably. "Oddly enough, though we couldn't hear for the din nor see for the smoke, yet it was a very moving and patriotic day." Then, she added wryly, "Though Liberty should be a *man,* with his vote and his independence."

When they finally reached Sherwood, Emily's guest did lay off her hat with a sigh and lean her head back against the chair for a few quiet moments. Emily soon discovered, however, that the almost tireless woman did not know how to rest. Even late in the evening, she would still be enthusiastically talking, while Emily struggled to pay attention.

"Does thee not get discouraged after so many years?" Emily asked at one point.

"We go forward only by inches," Miss Anthony admitted. "But you carried petitions for woman's property rights, didn't you? Each year we again carried in those petitions, signed by thousands of women, to those guffawing legislators in Albany. It took six years for the idea to percolate in those slow male brains, but they finally passed that bill. Now we're inching along toward Woman Suffrage and it will come too... eventually."

Emily looked at Susan, liking her very much, so earnest and sincere. She hesitated, then said, "Isabel calls thee 'Aunt Susan.' Would thee mind if I should do so, also?"

With a near-grin, her guest retorted, "Certainly I would not mind...Aunt Emily!"

They laughed together, but then Emily went on more seriously, "We were speaking of Elizabeth Stanton. Is it not odd that a woman so free in thought as Mrs. Stanton should have married?"

"Well, you know she and Henry struck the word 'obey' from her marriage vow, and she has never answered to 'Mrs. *Henry* Stanton.' But she admits it was a surprise to find herself cooped up, rocking the baby, while Henry strolled downtown without a care."

"And yet most people seem to think marriage is the end most to be desired for any woman," said Emily.

"Oh, I know. My mother was pitied until she attained the *advantages* of marriage, but I remember baking twenty-one loaves of bread for Mother's boarders one day." She added, with a mischievous look, "And I told one strapping fellow that I did not want to be any man's legalized servant. He was looking to marry a dairymaid for his *sixty* cows!"

Emily chuckled, but then putting her head to one side, she studied Susan Anthony. It was not surprising to hear that she'd had offers. The only surprise was that reporters should call her homely and angular. Emily impulsively said, "Thee is so much more attractive than thy portraits."

"Oh, it's my bones. How the camera can make them so sharp I do not claim to understand."

Emily liked the indifference with which she said it. What Emily liked above all was Susan's single-mindedness about the suffrage cause. Saying this, she added, "Admire Elizabeth Stanton as I do, she tacks on too many causes to our suffrage drive, to my way of thinking. Does thee not find that the linking of causes doubles the opposition to each?"

"I thoroughly agree." Susan sighed. "But Elizabeth gets impatient when she sees so many wrongs to be righted, and suffrage coming so slowly."

"Her ideas on divorce reform must have alienated thousands of women."

Susan Anthony smiled. "I expect so, but we've found controversy also stimulates. Horace Greeley once said that the vicious attacks by the press helped bring our struggling cause to the whole country's attention."

Emily ventured, "Thee mentioned Horace Greeley...."

Miss Anthony's smile crinkled her eyes. "Oh, I suppose you've heard how we mortified Horace with his wife's petition in that hearing. Well, he deserved that, after all we'd done at his urging to get Negro suffrage. And what a glorious hour! Horace was *so* furious!" Even now, she laughed like a girl at the memory, before adding, "It's still hard for me to regret it." She looked far into the past and her smile faded. "But we *were* foolhardy."

Emily hesitated before saying, "Thee will not mind, I hope, if I tell thee now how anxious I was over thine arrest for voting."

Susan Anthony nodded. "I didn't vote with the intention of getting arrested. However, my trial startled more women into recognizing their degraded position than a thousand of our speeches could have done." After musing a moment, she admitted, "Nevertheless, it was not comfortable, and I promise I will not do it again."

Then shaking her head, she said wryly, "I do fear Elizabeth is going to stir up another such hornet's nest. She keeps saying she wants to edit a *Woman's Bible.*"

"Oh, I hope not!" exclaimed Emily. "That would upset most of thy good suffrage workers."

"I agree. I try to tell her that wrangling over theology can only divide us."

As they rose from the supper table, Aunt Susan said, "I thoroughly enjoyed that meal. On my tours, many of the meals set before me swim in grease, and I almost never can get a Christian cup of coffee." Abruptly, she added, "Have you no women's group I could address?"

Emily said eagerly, "I wasn't going to ask thee that, after I promised thee a rest," but now she hastily assembled a group of Sherwood neighbors. As this spokeswoman for suffrage delighted them with her humor, and impressed them with her facts, Emily realized that what Susan needed was not rest, but financial backing.

While they were talking over the meeting afterward, Susan Anthony confided, "I've been trying to get Clara Barton to join with us. Everybody knows about her rescue work with the war wounded, and she's such a charming person as well. She has only to appear anywhere to fill a hall with cheering males."

"Oh dear, does thee want that?"

"What more favorable attention could suffrage get? Usually all we get are women."

Emily nodded thoughtfully. "She is not willing?"

Disgustedly, Susan complained, "Oh, she's all wrapped up in trying to get the United States to join that international war relief league."

"The Red Cross. Yes, I've read about that. It seems wonderfully worthwhile."

"Well, it seems to me," Miss Anthony insisted stoutly, "that securing the vote for thirty million women is more so."

"We need both, I believe," said Emily gently. Tactfully, she did not say that Miss Barton was wise to keep her Red Cross efforts clear of the suffrage controversy.

"Well, maybe, but *I* need help with the lecture tours," Susan Anthony lamented, and then fell silent. Emily, glancing at her, caught a speculative look aimed at herself.

Emily smiled but shook her head. "No, no. I see myself working right here in this county, arranging meetings, carrying petitions and giving out copies of Lucy Stone's *Woman's Journal*. When we finally get the ballot, our women must be informed so they honor rather than shame their position."

"Well, yes, that all counts," admitted Miss Anthony.

Emily added, "And sometimes I can help out with money."

At this, Susan's face lit up. "Then..." She hesitated.

"Yes, I've been thinking that's the way I can best help thee."

And thus simply, the two became fast friends and Emily became one of "Aunt Susan's" enablers.

Nov 20, 1886: The noise of the hammer and saw is still the refrain, and the end doth not appear.

The two-story addition she was having built looked very attractive, she thought, with its decorative touches. And she had decided to name her dressed-up mansion "Tanglewild" for her wilderness out back. But how tired she was of the mess. Would they never finish?

Jan 1, 1887: Carpenters left.

After a long winter of settling into the addition, she took up her pen again, a bit crossly:

Mar 20, 1887: An interregnum of nearly 2 months. I seem to be too busy to chronicle, and the events of my life not important enough.

A man and woman called. She has grown very stout and has lost her complexion.

Persons become uninteresting after they marry. Is it that they cease to strive?

Apr 21, 1888: In New York. William and I met Belle, Agnes, niece Blanche, and Prescott Dixon, a pinched weazen-faced person whom I admire as little as my niece does much.

Looking around her hotel room, Emily felt like saying, "Can this be I?" For, after five weeks in Bermuda with William, Hannah and Belle, they were now spending a week in New York City. Emily's pleasure, however, was marred by the presence of this young man whom Belle had met last winter when visiting the Sandwich Islands.

I am sure that I am not mistaken in my judgment of him. A noble character could not have such a face, such a whole. Well, I am disappointed, probably I should take it more seriously if he was not so ill looking.

As she wrote this, Emily again paused. What was it about this Prescott Dixon that seemed so...so *false*?

Well, there was the little incident she had accidentally seen, when he went out to hail a cab at the curb. Emily, preceding the rest of the party out of the museum, had seen a skinny little street dog coming too near his elegant trousers. She had also witnessed the irritable kick which he aimed toward it. Yet, as he heard the door opening, he had turned with such a gracious smile, it was like a mask clapped over his true feelings.

Was she misreading him, being unjust to him?

She had closely watched him back in their hotel suite, and she had seen no real regard for Belle. The girl, on the other hand, was eager to have their party bend to his wishes. And he smiled upon her so caressingly, he was as smooth as cream. *I can't bear him,* Emily thought. *But I'll have to, or forfeit Isabel's affection.*

After he had gone, Belle had eagerly turned to her aunt. "Mr. Dixon was an ideal person to show us about the museum, he's so knowledgeable, isn't he?"

"He does seem so," Emily had agreed, politely. Then she asked, cautiously, "What does he do, Isabel?"

"Well, he doesn't have a regular position. He was a wonderful student, but he's had no backing to get started, though he is versatile enough to do anything."

"Oh yes, I see." Emily had kept her voice carefully noncommittal, but Isabel, who knew her well, had shot a suspicious look at her.

"He may not have had the chance to *achieve,* but worldly success is not all, you know, Aunt Emily. I think he is as fine in character and spirit as he is in intellect."

If he had any gumption or pride, Emily thought, he'd find himself an opening and work himself up. But she had meekly nodded and kept the peace with her darling niece.

Luckily, having Agnes Tierney along, most of their jaunts were planned to show the girl about, and excluded Mr. Dixon.

Belle, who had encouraged Agnes to go on to Cornell from the Sherwood school, was hoping that, when she was qualified, Hepsibeth Hussey might engage the girl as a teacher. "They think well of her at Cornell," Belle had told her aunt.

From that time, knowing that Hepsibeth Hussey was privately dithering about retiring, Emily kept this ambitious and charming young candidate in the back of her mind.

Back in Sherwood, Isabel's mother, Hannah, remarked to Emily, a couple of months later, that a gentleman friend was coming to visit Belle.

Emily's heart fell sickeningly, but she said calmly, "Is it Mr. Dixon? For thee will remember I also met him in New York."

Yes, it was Mr. Dixon, and Hannah added that she looked forward to knowing him better.

Emily managed to behave well during the one visit he and Belle made to her home. Even so, she disliked him more as she saw Isabel smiling so warmly on him and looking so proud of his every utterance. He simply was not worthy of her regard. He was just such a pompous lordship as she and Harriet May had laughed over, at Cornell.

Isabel was a woman grown, and yet, so innocent and trusting about people. And Emily could say nothing to warn her. How was she to keep her tongue between her teeth for a whole week?

To her great surprise, two days into his visit Prescott suddenly departed. She saw Isabel looking downcast, and William was distinctly grim. Relieved and grateful, Emily asked no awkward questions.

At any other time, she might have ventured to show more curiosity. Now however, she was watching with highly mixed feelings, as the temperance drive turned into a demand for prohibition of all alcoholic beverages. How furious the colonel must be!

Women spoke out at meetings and women paraded, this summer of 1888. Frances Willard, the colonel's "Saloon Woman," demanded the outlawing of alcohol "in the name of boyhood bewildered, manhood betrayed, in the name of woman brokenhearted, and homes broken down."

The Boston papers must have been full of abusive and derisive articles about this revolutionary campaign. Surely he would break his long silence to write her angrily, "Temperance is one thing but prohibition is nonsense!"

Nearly as outrageous in the colonel's eyes as outlawing his glass of wine at dinner, would be the Prohibition Party's also demanding the ballot for women, and equal wages for equal work.

She could just hear him scolding, "You might have won on temperance, but you will never get woman's suffrage. When you tack a bad cause on a reasonable one, you lose both."

But still, no letter came.

Finally, when Emily visited her plantation, she wrote the colonel:

> *Teachers Cottage, Arcadia*
> *Nov. 2, 1888*
>
> *I am writing on the spot where 22 years ago you and I thought a house might stand for the home of a teacher. I am sitting alone by the open fire on the hearthstone.*
>
> *I am now contracting to sell the last of the land excepting the lot surrounding this house. Yes, and the extreme portion where you and I dined one day, I think.*
>
> *Country slowly improving. Contrasted with the dead level of ignorance when you and I walked about in this land, I realize the rise and progress of Va. is well started.*
>
> *Roads bad. If I were only going to be here another week, I would write all my neighbors, colored and white to lend a hand for a half day to better the highway and I would superintend.*

Emily had no time to fret over the colonel's failure to respond, for she and Isabel had plunged into suffrage work. When Emily was next asked to take an office, she proposed Isabel in her stead, and in 1890, her niece became secretary of the National Temperance Organization. Belle enjoyed this so much, Emily resolved to pass other such burdensome positions to her. Perhaps they would keep her too busy to think about young Mr. Dixon.

Now and then, Emily would wonder why, since Isabel was still writing to him, he never visited again. Emily did not want him to come, of course, but why was the romance hanging in this strange way?

While Isabel's interest in Prescott Dixon was a nagging anxiety to her aunt, Katy was a positive joy. She had more than fulfilled her early promise by speeding through Sherwood Select School's complete course, from bottom to top, in three years. Graduation day at Sherwood Select School that year was very special indeed, for Katy stood on the platform to receive her diploma. When Emily congratulated her on her excellent record, she answered, "I could not fail you, Miss Emily."

Now Emily was paying her college tuition, but she would work for her own board. Next, she was hoping to enter the Woman's Medical College of Pennsylvania. Emily knew she was going to miss Katy's quiet, pleasant presence at her table, and her help in the house. Still it gave her a keen pleasure to think that this woman would have the future she had so desired for herself.

Before Katy took the train for Philadelphia, she looked back at Emily and hesitated. Then she turned about and walked back to say earnestly, "Miss Emily, I owe everything to you. If ever you need me, you know you have only to ask, and I will come."

Emily's experience with the fleeting nature of gratitude led her to take this as merely a graceful remark. Nevertheless, each time she thought of it, she smiled affectionately.

Katy's achievement had been only part of Emily's satisfaction on graduation day 1890. It also was Hepsibeth Hussey's denouement as principal of Sherwood Select School. Though Emily valued that remarkable woman's work over the past nineteen years, at heart, she was delighted to take control, and her first step was to bring Agnes Tierney back to Sherwood as principal.

Now she felt welcome to visit at school, a pleasure after Hepsibeth's snubs. Just at first Agnes was anxious when making decisions, but Emily was soon able to assure Isabel that the girl was quite as competent as they had hoped, and a delightful companion in her home as well.

The next year, the Aurora bank wanted to recruit William as a director. He had become widely known during his two terms as state assemblyman, and to add to his attractions, he had also become a friend of Theodore Roosevelt. However, to qualify as bank director, he would need to buy some of Emily's stock in the bank. Instead, William suggested, "Why not ask Emily herself?"

When Emily was seated on that imposing and august board in January 1891, she became the first female bank director in the United States. Nevertheless, she was not too cowed to ask, tartly,

"How can you gentlemen trust a woman with such a responsibility when she cannot be trusted to vote?"

This same year, Emily was the state vice president for the Association for the Advancement of Women. Feeling, though, that opinions developed in local discussions, she and Belle and their neighbors formed an Equal Rights Association. Its members aimed to press for the ballot, and to become informed enough to vote intelligently.

From its first meeting, with Hannah as president, the Sherwood ERA included several men. Emily regretted this, in one way. Though men added interest, when they were present, most women would not speak at all. Even the brightest women clearly considered themselves less important than any male, however dull, or however idle his opinion. Or was it that they deferred, as Cornelia Hancock had said, to avoid the displeasure of the male?

Despite that one reservation, Emily welcomed the men to the Sherwood ERA. After all, equal rights could come only by educating males to vote for them. And they did add new viewpoints. Giles Slocum had been counting up female taxpayers in the town, and suggested the town should allow those women to vote. Emily, who now owned considerable property, naturally felt this was a sensible, if unlikely, proposal.

In the winter of 1892, Belle tickled her aunt by writing from Boston to enlist her help in a vacation course of lectures at Sherwood Select School.

> *It would be a sort of University Extension in Sherwood.*
> *They would not bring out large audiences, of course, but*
> *people who cared for such things could look forward to*
> *them with regularity. I always expect thee to agree with*
> *all my schemes. Hattie Mills will give Readings from*
> *Browning; Mr. Mills one on Emerson; Papa on Napoleon,*
> *and so on. Won't it be* recherché?

Emily chuckled, thinking of Isabel and Hattie May together in Boston, visiting the great suffragists, and putting their heads together to hatch this scheme. Of course, Isabel could count on her aunt's help. Most heartwarming of all was Belle's *thee*, a message of love in invisible ink.

At the closing session of Isabel's first summer season of lectures, she looked about the crowded room. "I could not have hoped for such an attendance! And we've had ten speakers of the highest attainments."

Her aunt teased, "If thee wanted programs that were choice and *in demand,* these certainly were *recherché!*"

In January of 1893, Sallie Hollie suddenly died. Carrie Putnam, even in her deep grief, wrote proudly;

> *The bitterest of our ex-slaveholders said of Sallie, 'That old Yankee ruined these people, making them think they are as good as anybody.' Sallie would have liked that for her epitaph.*

Carrie, that brave woman, would carry on the school by herself. Emily half envied her that niche in life where she had uplifted a whole community of blacks. But never mind, Emily's own woman's rights activities kept her more than busy.

Back in 1891, she had been elected president of the new county Political Equality Club. Now, she represented this club at a suffrage convention in Washington in February 1893.

While there, she was electrified by a black speaker, a freed slave named Jennie Dean, who was starting a secondary and trade school for black women in Manassas. This was to be just such a school as Booker Washington's twelve-year-old Tuskegee, in which Emily was interesting herself. She drove out immediately to visit and, liking what she saw, declared she would give $1,000 to finish paying for the school farm.

But shouldn't she be doing more to launch Jennie Dean's school, which was to train young black women to teach others of their race? With this idea planted firmly in her mind, she gave first a piece of land, and then the money to build a fine, large dormitory for women.

It was only after the building was nearly complete that she learned of Jennie Dean's saying she had not favored building that place, that "there was no sense in spending more than 400 dollars, as the cheapest way is the best way for us poor people." Jennie had also feared if Emily should die, they could not afford to refund the money. Nor did Jennie count on her continued support, since Emily was interested in so many other schools. Jennie had said, "We must not expect the sun to shine in at our door all the time."

This took Emily aback. Any other gift she had ever given a school had been eagerly received. But she now saw that in her own blind enthusiasm, she had launched Jennie into a much larger school than the woman had ever wished for. Emily could not help feeling the school could never have amounted to much in a $400 building, but she also saw she must assume a responsibility to see that the place survived.

Carrie Putnam, shortly afterwards, enclosed, with a brief, brave note of her own to Emily, a most puzzling letter from the colonel. He reminisced pleasantly about cooperating with Carrie, twenty-five years earlier, in fitting out the first Lottsburgh school building "by the yellow Potomac." He ended, "Does Miss Howland ever come back to revisit the scenes of her early endeavors?"

Emily put down the pages, knitting her brows in wonderment. How could the colonel write like that, as though he knew nothing of her Southern trips? Hadn't he been getting her letters? Could his mother possibly have arranged to have them intercepted? Puzzling over this, she could not reconcile sneakiness with the forthright Mrs. Folsom, chilly as she had been to Emily.

And then, a picture of Miss Folsom came to mind, with her trembling voice and her eyes sliding sideways.... And at last, Emily heaved a deep sigh. There was not one step she could take to remedy it, even if it were so.

Woman Suffragists

Emily Howland (standing)
with Susan B. Anthony, 1820–1906

Isabel Howland, 1859–1942
In 1891 she helped found the Sherwood
Equal Rights Association and the Cayuga
County Political Equality Club. In 1892,
she started work with Susan B. Anthony,
and in 1893, was Secretary, National
Woman's Suffrage Association

Harriet May Mills, 1857–1935
A lecturer on suffrage, she accompanied
Susan B. Anthony on her 1894 campaign;
was a suffrage campaign organizer in
California in 1895; Democrat candidate
for New York Secretary of State, 1920.

Forget-Me-Not: "Faithfulness"

1894

Luckily, she could immerse herself in her Equal Rights meetings. At one of these, her brother William described the new mechanical voting machine. In fact, William's response to the ERA had surprised and delighted Emily, for he was always glad to look up facts and give a brisk talk on any timely issue.

During his four years as an assemblyman in Albany, he had learned to be easier and less stiff. In that more cosmopolitan company, he had not only dropped his "thees and thous," but had also polished off some of his rough edges. Now he enjoyed speaking. Even more, he was glad to gratify his gentle wife, who was still the ERA president.

William would have done far more than speak to her meeting to please his dear Hannah, to whom he grew more and more devoted as the years passed. The looks they gave each other as William gathered up his papers after one of these talks were so eloquent that Emily felt a stab at having missed something so deep and fine.

Nevertheless, her life was very full. Her building, Howland Hall at Manassas, was nearly done and was to be dedicated in September, with the Honorable Frederick Douglass speaking. With much satisfaction, she considered herself to be a co-founder, with that strong and independent freedwoman, Jennie Dean, of the Manassas Normal and Industrial School.

1894 was also a very busy year for Emily and her two colleagues, Belle and Harriet May Mills.

However, no effort could be too great for Emily after the appreciation expressed in a letter written on July 27, 1893, and ending:

*Love to dear Isabel and Harriet May Mills, two of my
best nieces—best because they work so splendidly—and
ever so much to your own dear self.*

Lovingly yours,

Susan B. Anthony

In June, Emily represented her senatorial district before the Suffrage Committee of the State Constitutional Convention.

She lived up to her introduction at the Albany hearing as "a woman who is able to make an effective speech in three minutes." Among her brief remarks she said:

*Taxation without representation is tyranny. Have we a
representative government when one half of the people
have no voice in it? In the words of one of our poets: 'Go
put your creed into your deed, Nor longer speak with
double tongue.'*

The twenty-one women who spoke ignited no such explosion of rage as had Elizabeth Stanton and "Aunt Susan" when Horace Greeley had chaired this committee. Even so, the message to the Senate was the same: "No recommendation for suffrage."

Sitting at Emily's dining room table one evening shortly afterward, Hattie Mills jokingly called for a meeting of their "Great Triumvirate." "For here I am, with my friend Miss Emily Howland who calmly addresses august legislators, and my other friend, Miss Belle Howland, the secretary of the National Suffrage Association. I feel myself to be honored!"

"What nonsense," laughed Isabel. "Our third member gets to speak before the national conventions, while I merely take notes on what you truly important people say. And is it true you are to run the California campaign next year?"

Harriet shrugged. "Yes, but that's a year away. What I want now is to enlist your help with Aunt Susan's plan to speak at mass meetings in all sixty counties in New York State."

Emily exclaimed, "Excellent! She is such a logical speaker."

"Logical! Aunt, she sweeps them up like flies! There was never anybody like her for persuasion."

Emily quelled Isabel's frivolity with a mock scowl. "For moving an audience to indignation and emotion, I believe Elizabeth Cady Stanton is her superior. For persuading an audience by logic and facts, Susan Anthony has no equal. I should like to support that tour."

Harriet grinned, teasingly. "We hoped you might."

Emily chuckled. "Thee is an impudent child. Nevertheless, thee may put me down for...let me see...for $1,200."

Harriet gasped, "You will never cure me of impudence when it rewards us so munificently!"

Isabel said wistfully, "I expect Mama will want to contribute something, too, but I'm afraid I can do nothing."

"Think again, my girl," grinned Harriet. "Aunt Susan needs some good little drudge to look up tax records on the property owned in this state by women."

"Oh yes," agreed Isabel enthusiastically. "That's my kind of work."

Isabel did have the satisfaction at the state convention of hearing Aunt Susan quote her figures:

> *In 3/5 of upstate New York, female taxpayers own nearly 350 million dollars worth of property. And in Brooklyn, women pay a quarter of all the taxes.*

To the Sherwood ERA, Isabel modestly reported only:

> *The state convention in Ithaca was very successful although the people of Ithaca did not want it there.*

In February, Isabel, reporting on the 1895 National Convention, said Atlanta was a center for colored schools started by Northerners with Northern capital. She added, with an amused look at her aunt, "Despite the distress of the Southern people, 'Aunt Susan' Anthony went and talked to the students of the Colored University."

Emily chuckled at the vision this evoked of her stouthearted and persistent friend. "I can well imagine her doing so."

In that same spring of 1895, the state senate passed a resolution "looking to the submission of a Woman Suffrage Bill" 80 to 31, after "Aunt Susan's girls" fetched five clothes baskets of petitions onto the senate floor. When Belle reported this to the ERA, she added, "We can't look for an amendment this year, of course, but perhaps one year soon."

Emily clapped politely, but privately she wondered if it was possible, when even so liberal a man as the colonel took such a closed stand.

That fall, Hannah Howland planned an ERA program in honor of Elizabeth Cady Stanton's eightieth birthday, featuring a glowing tribute read from the *Woman's Tribune*, which ended:

> *Years ago she was the subject of ridicule, today she is a much honored woman. In the years to come she will stand side by side with Lincoln, as one of the liberators.*

Yes, it was true, Emily mused later. Not only had Elizabeth, with her friend and partner, Susan Anthony, orchestrated the collection of a third of a million petitions for Abolition. After that victory for the blacks, the two of them had steered the thirty year crusade for equality for women as well.

When she said this to Hannah, she added, smiling, "How pleased Susan Anthony must be. She always craves praise and credit for her friend Elizabeth."

At another of the Sherwood ERA meetings in 1895, Emily heard an account of the George Junior Republic at nearby Freeville. Boys and girls from New York City were spending their summers there learning self-government under Mr. George, with each working for the good of all.

Emily sat up when she heard "Daddy" George's motto: "He who does not work shall not eat." As she told Isabel, "I like industrial schools like Tuskegee and Manassas, and this is the only one I have heard of in the North."

Upon her querying him, William R. George wrote back:

> *This is a community made up of and governed by boys and girls between 16 and 21. They make their own laws and enforce them. They vote at the town-meeting and deal with their own delinquents.*
>
> *We have a very good school and each resident also gets a job in the farm or one of the shops (paint, carpenter, plumbing, printing or bakery.) This is real business.*

Emily asked to visit the Republic, and spent two nights with the girls in their rickety house. She listened to their past troubles and heard how this place was raising their hopes. After seeing the work the boys and girls were doing in their shops and classrooms, she told Isabel, "I'm all caught up in this place. I'd like to be a part of it."

Belle commented thoughtfully, "It sounds like the housing limits what Mr. George can do."

Emily said quickly, "Is thee thinking I might give a dormitory for the girls?"

Isabel looked a bit surprised but answered readily, "That would certainly be an excellent way to help, I should think."

When Emily went back for the dedication of the "Howland House," she remembered how the colonel had said of her Arcadian plantation: "Alms solve nothing, open no opportunities. This may answer." In the same way, this house would help these girls to help themselves.

In yet another Sherwood ERA meeting, Harriet May said of the 1896 California campaign, "I do not admit that we were defeated. Suffragists are like the English, never know when they are whipped."

As the laughter died down, she did admit, "It was the Liquor League that defeated us in California."

Emily looked around at the listening women. "That class of people who organize to fight woman suffrage have unlimited means and make a great show before the world. But they are still that same class that strove to keep their slaves."

Harriet said, slowly, "Well, after all, if the downtrodden had their rights, who could be forced to do the work that makes the rich richer? Or allows them to be idle?"

After Isabel and her aunt had taken a trip in the spring of 1897 including a visit at Tuskegee, Emily reported to the ERA: "Booker Washington is a marvel. His character shows forth in what he does. Isabel and I attended classes and visited the shops for women in dressmaking, millinery, cooking and laundry; and for the men, harness shops, shoe shops and so on.

"However, the feeling of the poor whites against the colored people is very bitter. The colored are not even allowed to ride in the same coaches with whites. It is easy to see where lynching sprung from."

Isabel rose as her aunt finished. "I want to pass around this picture I took of Aunt Emily at Tuskegee. She is standing beside the machine she gave the iron workers there. And also, Aunt Emily, do tell them what that speaker said that tickled us so."

"Oh yes," chuckled Emily. "He was editor of the *Rural New Yorker*. He said the Indian when oppressed stayed flat, while the more the African was pressed down, the higher he would rebound, and cut a pigeon's wing [dance step] in the air as he came down."

Arriving at an ERA meeting on July 20, 1898, to celebrate the fiftieth anniversary of the Seneca Falls convention, Emily marveled at the number of carriages around the Sherwood corners.

About fifty people listened to a panel which included Isabel and Emily, as they recalled the bleak prospects of women before that momentous meeting, and their advances in the half-century since.

Even so, Hannah said, as they left the hall together, "I know there has been progress but there is still so far to go..." And hearing the falling note of her voice, Emily cast a sharp glance at the thin face beside her, even as her sister-in-law added, "I don't feel I will be able to do much more work for the cause."

This struck a chill to Emily's heart at that moment. Later she convinced herself that Hannah had simply been tired and not herself.

During the last year of the century, Emily felt greatly encouraged by the Albany climate. This included a sympathetic governor and a female lobbyist, as well as several newspaper editors favorable to suffrage.

She was even more elated when she attended the International Council of Women in London and wrote home:

> *July 23, 1899*
>
> *Isabel was a true prophet though I did not believe her when she said that we should be presented to the Queen. I am glad that I saw her.*
>
> *It is such a pleasant memory that I shall have of a gracious, kind, intelligent looking old lady.*
>
> *We all returned to London, a weary satisfied lot of mortals. Had we not seen Queen Victoria and eaten in her house? These refreshments were by the Queen's special request, "those ladies will need a cup of tea and some refreshment." Yes, we had seen the oldest monarch in the world, whose reign had been the longest and the best in history. We had been royally treated in her home, our red letter day was done.*

Emily had just posted this letter in the hotel lobby when she met Susan Anthony. She exclaimed, "Could thee have ever imagined our taking tea at Windsor Castle?"

Susan, however, grumbled, "I had the highest hopes of our delegation being received by the queen. I was going to urge her to support full suffrage in England. It's inconsistent of her to say women should stay in their place, while *she* stands superior to every man in the kingdom. Well, I don't suppose I could have said that to her. But it was very pointed that she only nodded to us as she set off on a drive, whilst we waited in the courtyard for her underlings to summon us for tea."

Emily was more than satisfied with the lesser mark of royal favor. To think that she, plain Emily Howland of Sherwood, had seen the queen who had been sovereign during the terms of sixteen American presidents!

All this favorable attention had led to optimism among the suffragists. On Isabel's and Emily's parts it also led to pride in Harriet May's rise in suffrage work.

She was introduced at the New York State convention as "Harriet May Mills, state organizer. In whatever state she and Mary G. Hay have run campaigns, they have doubled the numbers of both members and activities. Miss Mills is a graduate of Cornell University and is devoting her youth and education entirely to the cause of woman suffrage."

As Harriet rose, she murmured to Isabel, "And thus step by step we gain on their lordships...we hope!"

Emily, who had caught that remark, afterward told Harriet how well she had spoken. Then gently, she added that she also had a "little scold" about the enmity the girls seemed to feel. "For it is easy," she cautioned, "to be sarcastic or to make fun of the way men hold onto their dominance. But mockery makes them feel we are enemies. They become angry and defensive, and even more opposed to giving us our rights."

Harriet said soberly, "We don't really feel enmity. After all, we couldn't do without the dear things, could we, Belle? I believe it's our way of keeping our end up." Here she smiled warmly at Emily. "I do see your point, though. You are saying sugar will get us more votes than vinegar," and all three of them laughed.

Emily and Isabel were even more proud of Harriet May as she swung forward to address the national convention. However, when Isabel praised her for her speech, Harriet May answered seriously, "What I do is always in the public eye. Not so with you, Belle, even when you sit on the national platform taking your minutes." Then with her impish grin: "We don't need to act like scullery maids anymore. Humility will never gain us our goal. Remember the lordly sex: they might have nothing else, but they have confidence!" Then looking about, she caught Emily's eye. "No, no! I mustn't say that, must I?"

After all Emily's glad expectations and all their meetings and campaigns, 1900 brought no advances. No new states granted women the vote.

And to Emily's dismay, Carry Nation went on the warpath with her axe, smashing saloons and making a spectacle of herself. "That woman's destructiveness will set the women's cause back fifty years," Emily groaned to Isabel.

And Elizabeth Cady Stanton's translation, *The Woman's Bible*, was another acute embarrassment as opponents of suffrage cried, "Heresy! Scandal!"

What a shame, Emily thought, that Lucretia Mott was no longer about to moderate, in her serene but powerful way, this latest of Elizabeth's "odd starts."

Elizabeth herself wrote impatiently in 1900:

Our movement is belated and like all things too long postponed, now gets on everybody's nerves.

As for Emily, she thought she could not abide hearing, one more time, some jokester hooting, "Oh, I believe in woman suffrage. Let 'em suffer!"

When "Aunt Susan" Anthony retired as president of the Suffrage Association, Emily complained to Isabel, "I think we are all discouraged. Half a century of effort and are we any closer to the vote?"

"Of course we are," Belle declared buoyantly. "You heard Aunt Susan speak of the attitude of the public against them fifty years ago, the hatred and rage. Now she is lauded everywhere. There are thousands of women ready to work for the cause. You cannot give up now!"

Though 1900 had been a disappointment to the suffragists, Emily knew she was helping women, in smaller ways, to progress. In 1901, after sending money to a school for blacks in Aiken, South Carolina, she wrote:

When one reflects that this money is to make brain power, the thought is inspiring.

Her satisfaction took a thump when Katy Munhall was refused her certificate to practice medicine in New York State.

Katy had written happily about her graduation from the Woman's Medical College of Pennsylvania, and Emily had rejoiced at her triumph. When the dejected young woman appeared in her sitting room with this news one day, Emily was thunderstruck.

"But why?"

"Oh, Miss Emily, because I didn't get a Regents diploma from Sherwood School."

Emily must have looked as stricken as she felt, for Katy's face crumpled with pity. Quickly taking her hand, she said, "Oh, Miss Emily!"

For just a moment, they clung to each other. Then Emily said briskly, "Well, there must be something we can do," and then more thoughtfully, "I wonder if we should not talk with President Frisbie at Wells College?"

Once they were in the carriage and on their way down the hill to Aurora, Emily felt quite recovered. Katy became hopeful, and rightly so, for with President Frisbie to vouch for the girl's education, New York State did certify *Dr.* Katherine Munhall to practice.

Emily felt pleased to her very bones. The success of her protégé went far toward making up for her own painful years of futile study and abortive hopes of practicing medicine.

In the midst of her elation, however, she feared for her school. For the first time, she saw how disastrous the lack of a Regents diploma could be to her graduates.

She was also a bit bothered, but much more puzzled, about Isabel. She had put her suffrage work aside to care for Hannah, who was now seriously ill. However, she was still quietly carrying on a correspondence with "that man."

Emily had not realized this until Belle was handed a letter by her maid, and quietly pocketed it without a word, but with an unhappy face. How odd this was, that year after year Isabel's romance neither warmed nor cooled. Emily had always been very careful to breathe no criticism of Mr. Dixon. However, now that she thought it over, she did recall the grim look on William's face after that one visit ended so abruptly.

Isabel was acting like the old horse that would neither go ahead nor stand still, but kept jumping up and down. Could her dithering be due to the old conflict between commitment to "the cause" and the demands of marriage? At any rate, Emily felt safe while Hannah was so ill, for Belle would never leave home while her mother needed her. Then abruptly this changed, in the late summer, when Hannah Howland died.

At Hannah's memorial meeting, Emily treasured the words of affectionate remembrance spoken out of the reverent silence. She shed no tears, however, for Hannah's death had come as a blessed release from her last painful illness. It was only afterward, when she was walking in Hannah's garden and thought, "Oh, I must tell her she has late lilies," that it struck her like a blow over the heart: "*Hannah is gone*! Oh, Hannah! What will I do without thee?" She sank down on the bench, her hands to her face.

Suddenly she felt an arm around her and Isabel said, brokenly, "Oh, Aunt Emily!"

Emily instantly turned to gather her into her arms. What was her own grief compared to Belle's, who had lost her "Mama"? Or to William's? It healed her a little to comfort Isabel, and later to think what she might do to help William through his nearly devastating loss.

A most welcome surprise lightened her deep grief:

Aug 1902: A letter from CWF. Strange he should write after so many years of silence.

> *He does not forget, neither do I. He is a noble, unselfish man.*

Later in the year she again recorded:

> *A letter from CWF telling of a life of self-sacrifice such as women often live, men rarely. Strange after 17 years the dropped thread, the broken tie is restored. He writes more frequently than in the past.*

In answering his first letter, she had not spoken of her suffrage work. Instead, by writing him enthusiastically of the grand work being done for blacks at the new Manassas school, she had intentionally reminded him of a deep common interest.

He immediately wrote back, wanting to give some books to the Manassas school library. Her delight had nothing to do with the size of his gift. After all, he could afford nothing on the scale of her continuing maintenance of the dormitory she had given. What he had really given her was the joy of knowing he still cared about sharing in her work with blacks.

She was now giving large sums of money to many struggling schools for blacks, and also to young people for their educations. And as her father had done before her, she made loans to her neighbors to buy farm machines or land.

And always, she and her colleagues pressed on for suffrage. As she said to Isabel, "We women can learn from the colored leaders. They are on the right track: educate, educate, secure competence."

Emily did not forget that only Father's legacy enabled her to support such causes. William had stopped one morning to take her deposit to the bank and was busily listing her dividends and interest receipts while she checked them against her book. She remarked, "Most people can't get a dollar ahead. But even while I am dispersing the interest from my investments, the principal is multiplying."

William, without looking up, responded, "Well, they say money attracts money. In solid investments, that is. This old railroad stock of Father's, for one, has always paid well for you."

"Money attracts money," she repeated slowly. "How inequitable! And yet it is no kindness to *give* money to people. The kindness is to give them a chance to support themselves."

Despite her belief in the seed-value of her loans and gifts, however, she did write:

> *I feel like nothing but a machine for handing out money.*

When Carrie Putnam visited at Christmastime, she had stopped first in Auburn, and came bringing Emily a "stars and stripes" from Harriet Tubman. "Oh, Carrie," said Emily as she unrolled the flag and laid it out over a chair, "can thee imagine that heroic old woman saluting me with such a tribute? That does make me feel humble."

"Well, I don't know why it should, I'm sure," protested Carrie, stoutly. "You certainly have been a doer for others ever since I've known you."

Dear Carrie! Such words from her were as good as a medal.

Later that winter, Emily accompanied Susan Anthony and Harriet May Mills on a delightful whirlwind tour of Tuskegee Institute and several other Southern industrial schools. Compared to these exceptional women, she rated herself low as a "doer."

Even so, she had to admit to herself that she was still a moving influence in the Sherwood ERA, and year after year the Political Equality Club reelected her as county president.

And to crown all, Emily was one of the women who went to Washington in 1904 to appear with Susan B. Anthony at a hearing before Congress. Each of them urged a different argument for woman suffrage. Standing before Congress and making her plea was one of the high moments of her life.

Emily had barely come back to earth when 1904 dealt her a blow which nearly overwhelmed her. After lurking around the fringes of her heart for thirty-eight years, irritating and yet charming her, opposing and yet caring for her, Col. Charles W. Folsom suddenly died.

At first she could hardly take it in. He had been in her thoughts a thousand times and more. She wondered now if she, as much as Mollie in wearing her blue gowns for her abominable lieutenant, had shaped her life to mollify the colonel. When she eschewed the lecture circuit in favor of less conspicuous suffrage work, was that for him?

In Emily's life, the colonel had been one of two cords tugging in opposite ways, the other being her fidelity to woman's rights. To cut either cord would have torn a piece out of her heart.

Well, it had only been a dream. Yet what a large part in her life that dream had played! As long as he lived, the dream had still been possible. At any time she chose, they could still have put out their hands and captured it.

She went to her chest of special treasures and drew out her cherished letter. Once more she would open the well-worn pages and reread the words already engraved in memory, words written by a hand now stilled, from a heart that had never faltered....

July 11, 1904: If I could but recall the past! Visited the garden and read my letter in pavilion. Written when he was quartermaster, I think in 1864, helping Miss Putnam about school purchases.

I think if I had done differently, I should not feel so unreconciled.

If I could only have seen him once.

Hyacinth: "Constancy"

1904

The next day brought a note from a sister-in-law of the colonel, whom Emily had never met. She enclosed a picture that he had left, designated for Emily.

This likeness was exactly as Emily remembered him. She sat holding it and her thoughts drifted to their happier hours: the evening he tapped his toe to the colored folks' "grand breakdown"; their rides together and their "PicNic" by the pool where the dragonflies were weaving dreams; the Sunday the "three carpetbaggers" visited the swamp and the pine woods, and his deep voice saying, "You've made Uncle Moses' dream come true"...and softly, "and he is not the only one."

Well, after all, Emily still had much to do:

July 30, 1904: Dr. Munhall came.

Aug 4, 1904: The last of Katy's visit. It seems very lonely without her.

Aug 5, 1904: I have been preparing blanks and writing personal letters to every WCTU in the county today.

She must finish this job today. Tomorrow she was to go to Ithaca to see William, Belle and Herbert off to Atlantic City.

Aug 6, 1904: Isabel sent word that her father thought it better to go in the noon train, so we were off. He bore going to Ithaca very well. I went out in p.m.

Got a neck ribbon because it was pretty for self. We were very comfortable at the Clinton House.

William had never really gotten over losing Hannah. Then this past spring, he had taken a hard case of flu which he could not throw off. Watching his drawn face as he slept on the train, it had struck Emily that the heart had gone out of him.

He hoped now to recuperate by the sea. Perhaps it might set him up again. After all, she told herself, William had inherited longevity and a strong constitution. Even so, as she returned home the next day after waving the three of them off in Ithaca, she felt vaguely uneasy.

Aug 15, 1904: Harriet May Mills urges me to be at the Fair on Woman Suffrage Day and speak.

Aug 16, 1904: Threshers will come tomorrow, Hattie Mills next day, the PicNic the next day. So we have a rush.

Sept 5, 1904: A letter from Manassas Normal and Industrial School saying the well is completed, cost $2,132.50. Depth 200 feet.

Affording 12 gal. to the minute.

Closing her diary, she drew her book to her and wrote the draft for her half of the well: $1,066. She hesitated over the cents, then wrote .00.

That week, after a call from a grateful scholar she wrote:

Sept 9, 1904: Rosie Lyon called this evening. Some of our girls treat me with attention, some with indifference. They little realize their debt to my effort for them, making their lives quite other than they would have been but for the school.

In all, with repairs and fuel it costs me at least $500. a year.

The next week Emily had a letter from her nephew Herbert, to whom she was no closer than when he was an arrogant upperclassman at Cornell. Nevertheless, she recorded anxiously:

Sept 15, 1904: Letter from Herbert in Atlantic City. He sees where his sister is and is alarmed, begs me to come.

It was not at all usual for Herbert to be solicitous about anyone except himself. This made it the more alarming that he wrote, "She's worn down with anxiety about Father, and all the sitting with him whenever the nurse is off-duty. This is just the time that fellow Dixon could work on her to marry him."

Emily thought this to be most unlikely. If William was ill enough for full-time nursing, Isabel would be the last person in the world to abandon him. If tired out and low in spirits, however, she just might make a promise to which this man could hold her. Was he the sort of person to threaten a breach of promise suit?

Oh, Herbert was infecting her with his nonsense. It was true, though, that Isabel's nature was faithful. It was more likely that this impasse might go on for years. My poor girl, she thought, and finished the entry in her diary:

> *I fear that there is no hope but a weary wearing out for her. It has all been wrong. I wonder if she will not regret wasting these years in mistaken devotion.*

Clearly, Emily must go to Atlantic City to help Belle in caring for William. However, she had two commitments she must meet. First, she had promised to spend two weeks with Harriet May Mills at the big women's convention in Boston.

The pleasure of Hattie May's company, of meeting old friends, and hearing fine speeches, dimmed under the memory of that earlier Boston meeting...those happy hours when she and the colonel had met for the last time.

She arrived home afterward with just enough time to prepare a speech to welcome the New York Woman Suffrage Association to Auburn. After a couple of days of writing and then cutting to the bone, she reminded her distinguished hearers that, in four western states:

> *women's opinions are counted at the ballot box, equal with their brothers. And the sky has not fallen.*

Her entire address was, as usual, rewarded with hearty applause. In her diary she modestly noted only:

> *Oct 18, 1904: Delivered my speech in Auburn.*

> *Among people present: Harriet May Mills, Carrie Putnam, Anna Howard Shaw [National Suffrage president], her secretary Lucy Anthony, William Lloyd Garrison Jr., Rev. Lyman Ward, Harriet Tubman.*

As she wrote this item, she considered the two missing faces. Elizabeth Cady Stanton had spent the last week of her life, in October 1902, in writing arguments for woman suffrage to President Theodore Roosevelt.

And "Aunt Susan" Anthony had also been absent today. When she had anxiously enquired of Susan's niece, Lucy had explained, "Aunt Susan's heart is acting up so I insisted she must not come down today. You know her too well, I expect, to imagine that she takes much care of herself." And she added, "I don't believe you've seen our home since Aunt Susan and Aunt Mary set up housekeeping, have you? I help keep them straight." She went on to issue a warm invitation to visit at 17 Madison Street when Emily was in Rochester next. "It would please them both," said Lucy.

Also Rev. Lyman Ward, principal of an industrial institute at Camp Hill, Alabama, had given her news of "Aunt Susan."

First he had mentioned his pleasure at having been on the platform with such honored names. "I am glad to know Harriet Tubman. I have always admired her remarkable exploits. I thought her quaint and weird."

Emily considered this curious appraisal with puckered brow. "She does have a fierce devotion to her life's mission, certainly. I have always envied her that single-mindedness."

The Reverend Ward remarked, lightly, "They say single-minded people are apt to be the world's saints."

Thinking of that determined, earthy woman, Emily shook her head decisively. "Harriet's no saint."

Accepting this with a nod, Lyman Ward had then turned the subject. "I called on Miss Anthony and when I told her I hoped to see you, she was quick to say, 'Don't ask her for any money. Emily Howland has been one of my chief backers for many years.'"

His smile was so contagious, Emily had found herself saying, with an answering smile, "Well, if thee cannot ask, perhaps I shall have to help thee without being asked."

At his look of surprise, she chuckled. "I have already heard of thine industrial school for young mountain people, from my friend Booker Washington."

It was true that she had helped to fund Susan Anthony's tours in recent years. This year she had also helped finance the publishing of Susan's monumental book (written with Ida Husted Harper), the fourth volume of *History of Woman Suffrage*.

More important to Emily than those projects, though, was any vocational school such as Lyman Ward's, usually for colored youngsters but, in his case, white. In what better way could she set poor young people on the road to independence?

Welcoming the dignitaries to the Auburn meeting had been her second commitment, and she was now able to go to Atlantic City to help Isabel care for William. Upon arrival, she found, to her startled dismay, that her brother had become very weak.

Almost as soon as she had her hat off, Herbert further startled her by drawing her into the sitting room to bluster, "That fellow is around here nearly every evening. I tell you, he's a fortune hunter! I calculate the old gentleman's estate to be worth half a million at the very least. When he's gone, she will be an exceedingly wealthy woman and well he knows it!" And at Emily's look of blank amazement, he stormed on, "Well, you needn't think I'm about to watch all that money go outside the family."

"So," she thought scornfully, "it's the money. That accounts for Herbert's solicitude. There's precious little to choose between him and Mr. Dixon: two elegant gentlemen with their pomaded hair and modish waistcoats and smooth white hands!"

Isabel, though calm and resolved, needed rest and time to herself. Emily was glad to relieve her by sitting many hours by William. Often, they talked of old times, when he was strong enough.

> *Nov 14, 1904: Herbert in one of his cynical moods and have had more than 2 hours of such revelations of pettiness as I cannot imagine a person living on: lack of attention to him in Cairo from Consul Morgan, the cousins calling Isabel "Belle", etc., lastly glorifying Southern manners.*

> *A letter from H. M. Mills thanking me for the gift. I got her a wrap.*

> *Nov 15, 1904: I visited with William. Herbert will not come over here to stay poor Isabel.*

One evening, as Emily sat by William's bedside, he suddenly asked, "Are Isabel and Herbert both out of the house?" Upon being assured that they were, he went on, "I realize I am not getting better and...well...I think you had best know the truth about Isabel and that Dixon. I only learned it myself recently, and I can't get it out of my mind. I don't know what to do."

Emily suddenly could hardly breathe.

"You remember Dixon coming to visit in Sherwood years ago?"

Emily nodded, her anxious eyes never leaving his face.

"Well, he and Isabel were sitting in the back garden under the big oak that last afternoon for a long time. When I went out to the carriage house, I could see them there on the bench, deep in talk, and I felt sure they were coming to an understanding. Then when I came back from my errand and put the horse away, I walked around that way. They were gone, but there under the bench was a whiskey bottle, small enough to have been in his pocket."

At Emily's gasp, he said harshly, "Everything hinged on that bottle! Because of it, I ordered the young man to pack up and leave.

Isabel was flabbergasted, of course, and never to this day has she known what it was I had found out about him. As a matter of fact, I did have him investigated. All I learned was that he's lazy and expensive, nothing worse, and nothing about misusing spirituous liquors."

The thought flashed through her mind that the same accusations could be made against Herbert. All that was forgotten, however, in her great relief that there was nothing here to discredit Isabel. But what was William working up to?

Gathering his strength, he went on. "Charlie Chase told me just before I came here that Dixon had been rude and overbearing to a young gardener we had at that time. This was a mischievous young chap and he admired Isabel and didn't want to see her marry such a fellow."

Emily anticipated breathlessly, "He put the whiskey bottle under the bench?"

William nodded somberly. "That's what Charlie told me. Dixon had nothing to do with it."

"Oh dear," groaned Emily.

He nodded agreement with her dismay. "I do not like the man. He is not the man for her."

"Oh, I agree with thee, William!"

"But," he continued sternly, "it is against our principles to employ a wrong method to accomplish what we believe is right." He looked at her questioningly. "You know what Belle is like, she's always for the underdog. If she knew he'd been wronged, it would drive her straight to him."

Emily envisioned Isabel's sympathy and outrage on Dixon's behalf if she should hear this story. "Yes," she admitted unhappily, "I am sure of that."

William said sadly, "I find it impossible to go on concealing the truth from her...and just as impossible to reveal it."

Sharing this dilemma had relieved William, but it stuck in her mind like a burr. How could either of them open up the old story and bring almost certain disaster to Isabel?

Well, at least she need not rush into any decision before taking a couple of weeks to go to Virginia. She was very reluctant to leave Belle, with William depending on her, and the other two trying to influence her. However, she had promised to dedicate the new well at the Manassas Normal and Industrial School. The arrangements were all printed up and she felt she must appear at this ceremony.

*Nov 30, 1904: Unveiled a window having inscription,
"Col. Folsom water plant, presented by Miss Emily
Howland of Sherwood NY 1904." The water plant is a
grand thing. Feeling glad that all has been accomplished
that I desired for so long.*

*Had Col. Folsom's picture hung in parlor, and told
students of him.*

How pleased she had been to tell these girls of the colonel's interest and gifts to the Manassas School during the past three years. Privately, she thought that though both she and the colonel had given as they felt able, his small gifts had strained his modest means in a way she had not known since Father died.

Even after his death, she thought, his gifts went on, for she had recently received a clipping from his sister-in-law from the *Boston Globe* of September 1904:

AUTOGRAPHS FOR PUBLIC LIBRARY

*Valuable Collection of the late Charles W. Folsom
Presented to City of Boston.*

*The Public Library of Boston has just received a gift of
more than 1000 manuscript letters of some of the most
prominent scholars and statesmen of New England. The
gift was made by the estate of the late Charles W. Folsom.
Most were written when Mr. Folsom was with the University Press of Cambridge. He was also secretary of the Phi
Beta Kappa Society of Harvard and was connected with
the Harvard Library.*

*It is a noteworthy gift and highly prized by the library
officials, the letters being valued at several thousands of
dollars.*

Thinking of his generosity, Emily had written that day to Belle:

*I am planning a library for this school to be named the
C. W. Folsom Library, and I shall add books to his collection as the years go by. He was one of the first helpers in
starting schools for freedmen, so it is a fitting tribute to
his memory, and one that I know he would like.*

This done, she returned by boat to both Carrie Putnam's school at Lottsburg and to her own Howland School at Arcadia. She had written earlier, at home, in her diary:

*Nov 15, 1904: Put CWF pictures in frames for Southern
schools. I could imagine him saying funny things about
my labor of love, and being hung in Southern school
rooms. I hope CWF knows what I am doing.*

At each of these schools, now, she told of the ways Colonel Folsom had aided it, and presented his portrait to hang over the blackboard.

At Carrie Putnam's school, after the ceremony, when the children and the townspeople were all gone, she suggested, "Thee is tired, Carrie, and no wonder. Do not wait for me. I'll just sit here a little while and then walk over."

Carrie trod wearily down the path, her birdlike look more pronounced than ever, and her shawl all awry. How lonely she looked, how frail and vulnerable.

Carrie, for thirty-seven years, and Sallie for twenty-five, had been outcasts among their own kind. Yet never, in loneliness, fear or grief, had Carrie swerved from her service to her friends. Watching now as Carrie trudged up the walk to her companionless home, Emily wondered if the colored people of Lottsburg had any idea what they owed to this staunch woman.

Then, turning back to the schoolroom, Emily studied the portrait. It was so like the colonel, she could almost imagine he would speak. He had been here in Lottsburg so much, helping Carrie in that first rude little school, she seemed to feel his presence now. Perhaps he was sitting on this front bench, as he once had in another such room, laughingly prepared to say his "8 times" table. At last, very reluctantly, she turned the key in the door.

Having now done all she could to keep his memory green, she took the steamer and train back to Atlantic City. Herbert met her at the station, obviously bursting with news.

"That fellow strutted in the other day, all full of determination," he began with relish, "but I needn't have worried. I might have known he couldn't push Belle around once she'd set her mind. I heard her say, 'I can scarcely believe you would press your suit when my father is dying.'"

At his aunt's look of surprise, Herbert had the grace to redden slightly, but he said defiantly, "Well, if you must know, I put my ear to the door."

Emily stared. What a creature he was! Yet she was no better, for while she could not bear to be listening to this, she was too anxious to stop his recital.

"Well! That dog had the gall to say, 'If somebody doesn't stand behind you, that brother of yours will have all your inheritance away from you.' And she said in a funny voice, 'This is all because of the money?' My guess is that she handed him his hat, because the front door slammed, and pretty soon she came out in the back hall all red in the face." And chuckling, Herbert added, "I'm just sorry I didn't see him going off with his smirk wiped off his face!"

When Belle greeted her aunt, she said ruefully, "I can imagine what Herbert has been telling you."

Emily, cautiously saying nothing, only looked at her anxiously.

Isabel smiled painfully. "Well, it's all true, dear aunt. Mr. Dixon showed his true colors, and the scales fell from my eyes, as they say." Then looking at her aunt's sympathetic face, she prompted, "Aren't you going to say you knew all the time?"

Emily shook her head slowly. "I don't want to crow over thee. All I've ever wanted for thee was thy happiness, dear Belle."

Isabel's face clouded over. "How different from Herbert. I don't believe he cares a snap for my feelings, he just didn't want the money to get away."

Emily was again too prudent to say anything to Isabel against her "little brother." How thankful she was, though, to see the girl undeceived at last and heart-whole, though chagrined.

William, on the other hand, she found to be very feeble but most deeply relieved that their quandary had resolved itself.

Often in the olden days, she had resented William and liked him less than Ben. He had made himself responsible for her, while she and Ben had supported each other in their times of trial.

Now how glad she was for these last few weeks to reach a warm, openly affectionate companionship with William, as equals at last.

"William," she said one day, "it's always bothered me that thee and Father were so secretive about helping the fugitive slaves. Once or twice I thought I was helping, and the outcome was like walking into a wall in the dark."

In surprise, he said, "That was a risky business and you always were a rash one. We were doing our utmost to save everyone's skin, the slaves', and ours, and yours."

"I wouldn't have been rash if thee had only told me about it."

"Emily, I never meant to be mean to thee." And with his use of the dear old pronoun and his holding his frail hand out to her, the last of her old resentment toward her big brother melted.

> Dec 27, 1904: I have read Helen Keller's essays with
> profit and amazement at her depth of thought and fin-
> ished style. It is classic. William has had a comfortable
> day.

Jan 5, 1905: Isabel had another hard night, her father requiring much care. Herbert did not come over from his hotel until later.

Herbert had come in reluctantly and after a cool greeting, he leaned sulkily against the window casing, tapping his foot impatiently. Then he arranged his tie before the mirror, and finally lounged over to the center table to stand, carelessly flipping over pages in a magazine.

Emily watched him surreptitiously over her book. How hard it was to like this young man, who thrived on admiration and envy but could not bear to be of use or comfort to anyone. He lived only to get, yet there was no contentment in him.

Belle now came in hastily. "Did I lay that book down here somewhere, the one I'm reading to Father?"

How worn the poor girl looked!

But Herbert snapped, "There's a big smear of lamp black on your face, Belle!"

Isabel smiled vaguely, unconcerned, though she rubbed absently at her face as she located the book on a little table by the window.

Even more irritably, he barked, "There's no need for you to act like a servant! He can afford nurses!"

Belle patiently answered, "I wouldn't give up these hours with Father for anything." Her face was exhausted, yet deeply contented as she went back to her father, carrying his book.

Herbert, on the other hand, angrily kicked a small footstool out of his way. Then he shot a suspicious look at his aunt, who was carefully absorbed in her book.

Jan 10, 1905: Isabel is nearly worn out. Herbert does not help. He is a thorn in the flesh.

She paused to look at what she had written, then crossed out the last line. One must try to be charitable.

Jan 11, 1905: William is feeble, keeps cheery. We bring up one and another scene or character of the distant past and he seems to enjoy the reminiscences. Isabel says he gets low spirited when I am not here. William talked much of gifts that he wished to leave in a will that he wants and Herbert bitterly opposes. Poor man. I wish that he had given himself the pleasure of giving in his life time. I presume he wishes so too now that life is all past. He loves life and would gladly live longer, but he is cheerful.

I think that the end is not far off.

Jan 13, 1905: I am so troubled over Herbert's attitude.

Their pleasant hours of reminiscing grew fewer as William grew weaker.

Feb 23, 1905: Our dear one left us this morning.
Though it is hard to learn to do without him I feel a deep
joy that he suffers no more.

To Belle, who tried to express what it had meant to have Emily with her, she said warmly, "My dear child, thee need not thank me. In these last weeks, thy father and I had such visits as never before." And turning to gaze out over the deserted boardwalk to the horizon, she added softly, "It is so fresh in memory, I can still hear the echo of his voice."

William was no more than brought home from Atlantic City and laid beside his dear Hannah than Herbert was proving himself to be quite as greedy and miserable as Emily had feared.

Mar 4, 1905: Herbert is a thorn in the flesh, a cruel one,
but Isabel must stand like a rock for her rights. He would
like to rule affairs.

I miss William in so many ways, social and business.
No one to talk of money matters with. I have no contempo-
rary who knew what I know.

Mar 26 1905: Herbert came in a snobbish mood. Does
not want any report of the Memorial Meeting. It seems to
me if the meeting had been under the auspices of persons
he thought are au fait *it would make a great difference in*
his feeling. I never realized before the power of this feel-
ing, not a particle of independent thought or action,
perfect subservience to what will the smart set think.

Herbert did not mind airing his annoyance over his father's will which named Isabel co-executor with him. He had wanted her to sign a waiver to let him act as sole executor. Emily had urged, "Don't give up thy rights," for then Belle could try to insist on their honoring their father's wishes. Both Emily and Isabel knew Herbert would not do so, if allowed to act alone.

Suspecting her part in this, he was barely able to be civil to his aunt. Shortly thereafter, perhaps deliberately in Emily's hearing, he snarled to Belle, "I'm ashamed of aunt's 'thees and thous.' She's so proud of calling anyone 'thee', no matter how high or influential."

Isabel hushed him, of course, and hurried him away. Emily, hearing her door close as they left, told herself it was merely the meanest thing he could think of. Later, however, she began to wonder uncomfortably if perhaps that impudent young man was right. Was she proud to set herself apart, perhaps even to seem better than others? And from the intense discomfort this idea gave her, she resolved to give up "thee and thou" except when speaking with other Friends, or close acquaintances.

> *Apr 1, 1905: Many notes and mortgage payments. So many callers every day, so many requests for money, to renew mortgages, or to reduce them.*

At a Sherwood Equal Rights meeting that fall, Emily gave an account of her recent trip to the convention in Portland, and then to Alaska afterward. She spoke of the ridicule Seward had endured for his purchase of Alaska. The recent discovery of gold and the great revenues flowing in from the territory had now vindicated him.

Though she did not mention it, she was tickled by this reminder of Father's "slight madness" for acquiring land, which had nearly always proved profitable.

At another October ERA meeting, a neighbor described her summer at Little Deer Isle off the coast of Maine.

Belle exclaimed right out loud, "Little Deer! Oh, I beg your pardon, Lucy. Do go on, please."

Lucy asked quickly, "Do you know Little Deer, Isabel?"

"No, I've never been there. But you remember, Aunt Emily, Aunt Louise buying a property on Little Deer a few years ago?"

Yes, Emily recalled this very well indeed, with her usual dislike for anything Ben's widow had done. Nodding, she said only, "Well, continue, Lucy."

The day after the meeting Isabel said to her aunt, "That place sounds most beautiful. The Catskill cousins, especially Blanche, are always asking me there summers. Hattie May and I are usually all tied up in campaign work, but I must say, Lucy's description makes me long to see it."

Emily said decidedly, "It would not do for me. I discovered long ago I cannot bear a quiet life."

At yet another meeting that fall, Herbert held at least the female portion of the ERA meeting enthralled by his account of his 1903 cruise in his yacht from the South Seas to Hong Kong and Japan, and on to Australia. Herbert always thrived on adulation, of course. These ladies were as impressed by the attentions showered on him by the dignitaries and the socially elite at each stop as even this conceited young man could wish.

How charming he was being, thought Emily, eyeing him and re-membering how ugly he had been just months before in Atlantic City.

Oct 24, 1905: Went to Rochester to Suffrage Convention. Read report as County President.

Anna Howard Shaw spoke. Harriet Tubman arrived and sat in station all night. Ladies received her cordially. I visited Susan B. Anthony.

Meeting Harriet Tubman, Emily had greeted her easily, "Good morning! I hope your lodging was quieter than mine. A dog barked all night behind the hotel."

"I sat in the train station last night and stepped over here to the hall this morning," Harriet had answered calmly.

"Harriet! You sat up all night?" Emily had gasped in dismay.

"That's all right, ma'am. Don't you worry none. I's used to sleep-ing anywheres I can."

Emily had cast her mind back to her arrival the night before. Harriet had obviously been on the same train, for they had met on the platform. Emily had spoken to her and then thoughtlessly seen about her own luggage and a cab, forgetting all about the poor woman. Oh, why hadn't she asked where she was staying? Or of-fered her a ride? Hot with shame, Emily had declared, "That will never happen again. You can always share my lodgings."

"You'd share a bed with me?" Harriet had stared. "Land, I believe you means it!"

"I do," Emily had said staunchly. She was perfectly aware that however much she admired her, Harriet would be an unconventional and uncomfortable roommate. All the same, such a heroine could not be left sitting up in a station all night. "I do mean it," she had repeated, nodding her head sharply.

Harriet, with a wry grimace, had retorted, "They ain't going to let me in any hotel you'd stay in."

Interrupted then by the beginning of the proceedings, Emily had stepped toward the platform. She had vowed, however, to have a word with Hattie Mills. When planning future conventions, they must find a hostess liberal enough to welcome Harriet for the re-markable woman she was.

When she had mentioned this to Harriet May, during a recess in the convention, the girl had first asked, in dismay, "Are you angry with me?"

Emily had stared. "I? Angry with you?"

"There you go again. You've always said 'thee' to me."

Emily had chuckled and explained her new resolve.

"Well, I wish you will make an exception for me," Harriet May had grinned. "Otherwise I'll always be afraid you don't like me anymore. Now, what were you asking me?"

Having heard how Harriet Tubman had spent her night, Harriet May was as struck as Emily had been, but said, "She probably is right about the hotels. I wonder. I believe I'll talk to Aunt Susan."

"Why, I am planning to call on her myself, after this meeting," Emily had said.

And when, indeed, she did call at the modest brick home on Madison Street and the door opened, she smiled, "Well, Aunt Susan!"

Emily looked with affection at this splendid woman. Susan had been lauded in Berlin at the 1904 International Council as "not just America's 'Aunt Susan' but Susan B. Anthony *of the World!*" Yet here she stood, smiling broadly, as unaffected as ever.

"Well, Aunt Emily! Come in!" and she threw the door wide and proudly showed her guest in. "Isn't this a neat little nest, after all my wandering years?"

"How comfortable this is. I am glad for you, though I have always enjoyed having you at Tanglewood," returned Emily warmly.

Susan stopped and peered at her. "I thought you called your home Tangle*wild.*"

"Oh well, Isabel talked me around. She said I've tamed the wilderness."

Susan laughed, but then added sincerely, "That's a grand lassie you've got there!"

These words gave Emily the deepest pleasure. And as Susan now continued to show her about, it was also with pleasure that she admired all their arrangements, and especially Susan's office which she termed her "headquarters."

When Emily went on to ask for advice about housing for Harriet Tubman, Susan Anthony's brow clouded. "I've asked her time and again, and she knows I mean it...and yet you see she won't come. She always says, 'No lady wants the likes of me in her house. Don't you worry none 'bout me!'"

Having shaken their heads over Harriet Tubman's independence, they settled down to talk over the events of the day. Emily mentioned Elizabeth Stanton, saying, "Someone referred to her today as the Mother of the Suffrage Movement."

Aunt Susan laughed. "She wouldn't care for that title. Poor Elizabeth had more than enough motherhood before she got her seven launched and was free to work again. I would rather say she was the rock on which it was built."

"You were a team," said Emily earnestly. "If suffrage ever comes, it will be at least half due to you."

Susan shook her head. "We could never have hoped to do it without all of you."

After a thoughtful pause, Emily asked, "You do gain a little support for your proposed federal amendment, do you not?"

"Now, now!" Miss Anthony held up an admonishing finger. "As I keep telling 'my girls', it is *not* the Susan B. Anthony amendment. I did not write it nor introduce it into the senate. To Elizabeth Stanton and Senator Sargent be all credit!"

Emily nodded, "All right, I'll remember." Then she repeated, "But is it gaining?"

For the first time, Emily saw the fine old face discouraged. "I don't know. I told the senate committee a year ago that we have been waiting for thirty-five years. First we stood aside for the Negro. Then we waited for millions of immigrants. When is our turn, I asked them. And their answer is still a stubborn silence."

Emily remarked, "If I could have voted in 1864, I would have been proud to cast my vote for Abraham Lincoln. Since his death, I've been so ashamed of his party, I always think of myself as a Democrat."

"I quite agree," said Susan sharply. "By refusing the vote to the Southern whites and to all women, black or white, the Republicans perpetuated their reign for twenty years, more shame to them!"

To lighten Susan's most unusual gloom, Emily said, smiling, "I have some useful information for you. A speaker at our ERA said large men are more apt to favor woman suffrage than smaller ones."

Susan Anthony's eyes lit with amusement. "Well! Now *I've* observed that naturalized male immigrants oppose it, almost to a man."

Lucy Anthony, who had come in during their talk, put in, "And didn't you say, Aunt Susan, that Southern men are more in favor than Northerners?"

Susan laughed heartily. "Well, taking all this together, if we concentrate on getting every large, native-born Southern male to the polls, our victory should be assured!"

Their laugh over, Emily said, "I am curious. Harriet May hinted at a story about a shawl of yours."

Susan immediately chuckled again. "You surely do remember my red shawl that I've worn on the platform at every convention, all these many years?"

Emily nodded, smiling. "Of course."

"Well, once when I blossomed out with a new white one, a reporter called out, 'Where is the red shawl? No red shawl, no report!' So Lucy, here, ran and got it for me, and everyone laughed and clapped as I put it on. Such fun!" Her old eyes sparkled at the memory.

Happy to leave on this note, Emily rose but paused to ask, "Will we ever get New York State?"

"New York is the hardest nut of all to crack," admitted Susan. "I wonder how many hundreds of washbaskets of petitions we've carried into those Albany chambers in these fifty years!" But then brightening up, she tallied, "Wyoming, Colorado, Utah, Idaho...four have come in. You mark my words, Aunt Emily, it will come!"

Nov 9, 1905: Packing boxes of clothing for South. Now I think I can feel easy in the consciousness of doing what I can to clothe others for winter.

For one of the November ERA meetings, Emily shared ex-President Grover Cleveland's objections to women's clubs, as listed in the *Ladies Home Journal:* He feared women would neglect their homes, and would be led to want the vote. And he said that woman's lack of logic was her greatest charm!

Emily also quoted Alice Blackwell: " Mr. Cleveland sees man as the human race and woman a gift to it, her sphere being ministration to man."

Dec 4, 1905: Charley and George Howland have bought the brick Meeting House for $250 and it will be converted into a barn. It really saddens me. I have sat so many hours of my life in it, motionless as a statue, while silence reigned.

She put down her pen, seeing in her inward eye the small Emily sitting in the painfully hard pew, with no back except the board that came across behind her head. How difficult it had been to keep her mind from her new silk frock. Yet thinking of it would be vanity. And how hard it was to keep from moving, to ease her discomfort. If she wiggled her toes she could keep the rest of her still, she had learned. But an hour and a half was so endlessly long to sit...and sit...not fidget...not move at all...and not think of the new silk dress.

Not only was Emily distressed at the closing of her old Meeting House, but she faced one more grief.

Isabel came in one March day, with newspaper in hand, wiping away tears. She said unsteadily, "Oh, Aunt Emily. Aunt Susan is dead!"

There was a long silence while Emily, with bowed head, tried to realize it. Her mind flew back to the dozens of meetings that she had heard Susan Anthony address, to the many petitions Emily had carried at her old friend's request, and to their many warm and stimulating chats.

Isabel, reading from the paper, added, "It says her last public words, at her eighty-sixth birthday celebration in Washington last month were: 'Failure is impossible!'"

Emily looked up at that and said tartly, "Then you younger women will have to see to that. I can't do any more."

Hollyhock: "Fruitfulness"

1906

That spring, Emily met discouragement everywhere. All her grand old colleagues were gone, save for Cornelia Hancock. The drive for suffrage seemed to be stalled. She complained sadly to Isabel, "The speeches now are all echoes from the past."

Her discouragement was perhaps deepest with the Sherwood school. Its enrollment was now tiny because its graduates, lacking Regents diplomas, were turned away from colleges and normal schools.

Still, in July she wrote to greet Carrie Putnam on her eightieth birthday:

> *However far from our ideal in achievement or in the*
> *spiritual life, we have meant well to humanity and we*
> *intend to be doers and seekers to the end.*

In January of 1907, her summary to the ERA of the governor's message included the news of Will Letchworth's giving the deed of his substantial tract, including the three-mile long Genesee River gorge, to New York State for a public park.

Amid the murmurs of "Isn't that wonderful?" one woman explained to another, "He's Isabel's uncle, you know. He was Hannah's brother."

To Emily, who had known modest Will as a boy in Sherwood, it was even more amazing. She did not say to them that she remembered him arriving afoot for a weekend with his family, back when he was earning less than four dollars a month in Auburn.

She did go on, however, to tell them of Will's desperate struggle to save his gorge. A corporation had intended to dam the river for electrical power, cutting his three great waterfalls to mere trickles. She told how the governor had first promised to protect this natural wonder and then, pressured by several legislators intending to profit from the scheme, had betrayed Will.

Only by making the tract over to the people of New York had Will managed to save his thousand and more beautiful acres from industrial predators.

Emily did remark also that President Theodore Roosevelt's message to Congress that same month agreed with Will Letchworth's fight to keep his land wild. For, as the president said:

> *To waste, to destroy our natural resources, to skin and exhaust the land...will undermine in the days of our children the very prosperity which we ought to hand down to them amplified and developed.*

In thinking over this meeting, Emily's outrage over poor Will's treatment was of a piece with the rest of her discouragements. Still, she kept doggedly on with her meetings. And by the next year she was again enthusiastically addressing the Political Equality Club, as its president for the seventeenth year. After listing several nations where women had finally won the vote in 1908, she said:

> *In the past seven years, more women secured full suffrage than in all the previous century.*
>
> *It is in the air, this awakening of women.*

Late in the winter of 1909, Emily and Cornelia Hancock visited eleven colored industrial schools throughout the South. This was Emily's third visit to Booker T. Washington's Tuskegee Institute, where his teaching of practical trades and skills set the standard for the other schools. How she did admire that man!

And while they were visiting at Manassas, she gave $500 for a cow barn. Her heart wished to give the money for library books in the colonel's memory, but her head decreed that their crying need was the barn.

From New Orleans, she and Cornelia took the train on to California for a sightseeing visit, touring Los Angeles and Escondido, hidden between mountains, and on to San Diego through wild country, by stage.

Much as Emily loved Cornelia and enjoyed her company on this long trip, there were reticences between them. They could compare their colored schools and the different outcomes of their two plantations. And Cornelia could tell of her trials and joys in starting first a Family Society and then a Children's Aid Society in Philadelphia.

Now she was agitating for sanitation and schools for a nest of squalid houses known as Wrightsville.

Emily burned to ask if Cornelia had bled inwardly at cutting the bond between herself and her reckless young doctor. Or was she truly the heartless creature she had once declared herself? It was admirable that she was strong enough to have cut him off and gone on, unencumbered, with her work. Yet how well matched they would have been, those two heroic young people!

And most of all, Emily would not mention the colonel's name. How could Cornelia, resolute in her renunciation, ever understand Emily's caring for him for thirty-eight years, and missing him long after he was gone?

Amid their reminiscences, Cornelia asked, "Did thee ever meet Mollie Martin of late years?"

"No, our acquaintance languished during her marriage and we never renewed it." Reminded of Mollie, Emily mused, "I wonder if she ever took up suffrage work?"

"I hope not," said Cornelia crisply, and at Emily's look of surprise, continued, "unless, of course, she regained her sense of humor. Nothing sets people against a cause like an angry person haranguing for it."

With her spirits revived by her trip, Emily now determined that the Sherwood school graduates must receive Regents diplomas. For as she said, "The light must not go out." Somehow these young people must have their chance. So she set out to meet the difficult demands of the Regents Department.

On the opening day in September 1909, she was rewarded as she and Belle stood at her south window watching the vehicles streaming into the school driveway, though they would not know until later that fifty-three young people had enrolled.

Isabel turned from the window and looked at Emily with shining eyes. "Dear aunt, I've heard many famous bells in many lands, but never one so beautiful as your school bell this morning, calling these youngsters back."

Her aunt, though equally joyful, was always practical. "Well, this repays all my struggles with that aggravating Education Department."

During this fall of 1909, Isabel was full of a new plan to enlarge her father's home, making it elegant and gracious and renaming it Opendore.

Emily enjoyed all the planning and the stir and bustle. Though she gave quantities of advice, Belle did not take most of it, for she was by no means of her aunt's economical turn of mind.

When Belle first displayed her plan, Emily declared that one huge room on the northeast corner was ridiculous. "Thee does not want any great drawing room like that! Thee wants a cozy sitting room looking out on thy mother's flower garden."

"But I do want it, Aunt Emily! It's my ballroom."

"Thy *ball*room!" Emily stared at her in such blank amazement, Isabel could not help laughing.

"Are you imagining I will have rowdy Saturday night dances as they do at the dance hall in Scipioville?" she teased.

"I do not understand at all. What possible use could thee have for a ballroom?"

Isabel was still laughing softly, but at her aunt's cross look she quickly sobered. "Dear Aunt, I know you have a picnic each year for the students of your school, but I should like to have an indoor dancing party for them." And seeing Emily considering this with equanimity, she added, "And think how pleasant to have our women's meetings or receptions in a room big enough to be comfortable."

Emily turned this over in her mind.

Isabel prompted, "Would it not be pleasant?"

"Perhaps so, but think how expensive it will be. Could thee not cut it by a third?"

And as the work went along, Emily frequently found herself again demurring over some detail.

"Brass door knockers!" she exclaimed in amazement. "Why, this one is of Shakespeare! And here is Mr. Pickwick."

"Yes, for the doors to my Shakespeare Room and my Pickwick Room."

Emily snapped, "Can't people use their knuckles?"

Belle laughed softly. "Dear Aunt, you thought the world would come to an end when I had William Weyant take my new winding staircase all apart and rebuild it. But you see how lovely it is now. I see just what I want in my mind and it's important to me that all these details be just so. I want my home to be charming and elegant and welcoming."

Emily muttered, stubbornly, "It could be that for a third of what thee is spending." After regarding her niece who, head on one side, was smiling coaxingly at her, she finally heaved a deep sigh. "Door knockers! Well, all right, but what will it be next?"

Even when they disagreed, it was pleasant to sit with their heads together over the plans of the house. Emily was so thankful to see Belle heart-whole and happy again that even when she did not approve of her niece's extravagances, she was indulgent with her nonsense.

For herself, life was always full of her affairs, large and small, and right now she was interested in the Piney Woods School.

Back in the spring of 1910, a letter with a Mississippi postmark had arrived. "Another begging letter, I suppose. Well, I cannot support any more schools," she had grumbled, impatiently tearing it open. Then, her attention caught, she had read it carefully.

"Can thee imagine this, Belle," she had exclaimed, "a young Negro man, well educated in the North, actually going back to Mississippi and braving the hatred of the whites to start a school for illiterate colored sharecroppers? And with only $1.65 in his pocket!"

Seeing that she had caught Belle's interest, she had added, "He says he started with ten students in an old sheep shed. Now, in less than a year, he has eighty-five people mastering their letters and figures, and learning practical skills."

"That sounds like a man and an opportunity you can't ignore," Isabel had said, smiling at her.

At first Emily had thought she would have to ignore it, for she never felt right to touch her principal. And yet Laurence Jones and his Piney Woods School kept coming back to mind. Especially was she reminded of him when she read a letter which Herbert had written to Belle from Paris, where he now kept his permanent address.

Emily remembered how Herbert had huffed about getting every penny of his half of his father's estate. He had even refused to let Isabel make the gifts of her father's desiring, before splitting the residue. This letter was a curious mix of his usual discontent and his usual crowing over the compliments and attention he was receiving from the smart crowd in that sophisticated city.

Herbert's abundant wealth, his yacht and world travel and all his diversions never satisfied him. Remembering Belle's contentment in caring for her father, Emily had thought, "Blessed are the givers."

And suddenly she had scrabbled in her letter basket for the Piney Woods plea. After reading it once more she had dipped her pen and written:

Although I am supporting all the schools I can, your story appealed to me in a special way.

Enclosed is a check for $15.

Emily Howland

When Professor Jones had written to thank her, he had said her response was the only one he got from his first hundred letters. It gave him hope, he said, that his special story would gain support if he could only reach the right people.

Jan 5, 1911: I wrote several letters and scattered over $1,000. to help civilization.

"The Little Professor of Piney Woods" had haunted Emily all the past year, since she sent that first check. He was teaching his colored people precisely the skills they needed to be independent. It was just her kind of work. And she knew he needed a way to get his message out to those who might support it.

So today she had sent a second check with the request that he buy a hand press and issue a school paper. She had added that she would like to receive news about the school, regularly.

Professor Jones soon reported that the press stood in his own cabin, and he was teaching students the art of printing. Also, he reported that his enrollment had soared to more than a hundred.

Mar 21, 1911: An appalling event. Booker Washington has been assaulted and seriously injured, while looking for the number of a house where he was to meet a friend. A man rushed out and struck him a heavy blow which made wounds for the surgeon to dress. I think there is no man in U.S. whose going would be such a loss to the country as his would be.

May 28, 1911: Packed a large barrel for Howland School, Va.

June 5, 1911: Suffrage meeting in Auburn. I spoke and succeeded better than I expected. Felt as a speaker always can, that my hearers were interested.

June 13, 1911: I am begged to a frazzle.

July 14, 1911: Dr. Katy Munhall's expressions of affection are touching. They evince such gratitude as few persons are capable of.

To have this favorite young friend visiting her was a delight. Katy told first of her work at the telephone company in Buffalo. Then she said earnestly, "Please remember, if ever you need me, I will come.

What would I be doing now if it had not been for you? Still opening the door for some doctor's patients, I expect. I can never forget what I owe you."

Aug 9, 1911: Isabel and I came to Little Deer, Maine.

Emily had come with Belle mainly because Cornelia Hancock was going to be there, too. Now she was sitting on a large rock, overlooking Swains Cove below, but looking out at the bay and its islands and beyond to the Camden Hills rising on the mainland. Belle, beside her, dreamily watched the gulls wheeling over the water glittering in the afternoon sunlight. Somewhere behind them, a white-throated sparrow was singing in a field, adding a sweetness to the quiet, companionable moment.

Finally Isabel turned to smile at her. "I'd like a cottage here sometime. I even know where I'd build it, up past Long Cove." Then she rose reluctantly. "If we don't hurry along down to the landing, Cornelia's boat will already be in."

How delightful it was to find Cornelia as plucky and warmhearted as ever, and no more than Emily did she want to sit and rock. Their days together were filled with walking, sailing, hunting for berries and, for Emily, always keeping an eye out for unfamiliar flowers.

One afternoon, having picked enough berries for their meal, she was watching her friend who was bent nearly double and raking vigorously for clams with a curiously short-handled tool. Cornelia straightened up, looked about her, and said, "I love this place! I was thinking, wouldn't this be a top-notch summer retreat for all our friends? Think of all the women who toil in a hot, dusty, smelly city. Wouldn't this brisk air just set them up? And walking in these woods, wouldn't that be good for anything that ails them? I'd buy this whole island if I could." But then, pausing to pick up her bucket, she added, with a grin, "But there are other delights in this world, like steamed clams and blueberries for supper."

Aug 31, 1911: Back to Boston, went to Parker House where we were very comfortable, not overwhelmed by the smart showy set.

Visited Longfellow's home, including kitchen, where the cooking utensils reminded me of my own early days when tin ovens, skillets, etc., were in vogue.

Sept 1, 1911: Isabel and I walked in public gardens; auto ride to aviation scene. It was a thrilling sight to see them rise and soar out of sight. On to Framingham (27 miles.)

Arrived back in Boston at 8 p.m. Went to a movie after supper. A full day and a weary one.

Sept 6, 1911: School opened with 54 pupils. Over-whelmed am I with begging letters. Perhaps they think that I am so old they must all pitch on me now.

However, her imagination had been caught by the happenings reported in the printed bulletins from "the Little Professor of Piney Woods." Without being asked, she had sent a third check, telling him to buy a larger press so the school could put out a proper monthly newsletter, especially to people of means who might give support.

The prompt arrival of Issue No. 1 of the *Pine Torch* proved that her new press was in use.

Oct 13, 1911: Harriet May Mills telephoned me of the victory of Woman Suffrage in California. It seems too great to be true. It is the greatest gain that we have ever made...a large populous state. Finally the other states may follow. What a different world it will be.

Emily would not have blamed Hattie May if she had crowed over this as a personal triumph, after all her years of organizing state campaigns. However, when she and Isabel stopped in a few days later to rejoice with Emily, Harriet May said only, "Our first campaign was sixteen years ago in that stubborn state."

Belle merrily responded, "The scullery maids are gaining on their lordships!"

And Harriet hastily added, with a sideways grin at Emily, "But with no enmity." Emily chuckled. That rascal, Harriet May! She was now vice president and newsletter editor for the state suffrage group, as well as a national organizer and speaker. For all that, she was still just the same zestful, lovable girl at heart.

Oct 18, 1911: Isabel and Hattie Mills started for Suffrage Convention in Louisville. Once I should have gone. Now I prefer to stay at home.

Oct 31, 1911: To New York Suffrage Convention in Ithaca.

At the meeting at Sibley Dome, Cornell President Jacob Gould Schurman spoke. He said, in such a patronizing manner as made Emily squirm with annoyance, "Women have as much right to vote as men, if they *want* to vote." He might as well have added, "But why should they want to?"

Up popped Harriet May Mills to reply that women should vote whether they want to or not...that medicine was not withheld from the sick just because they didn't want to take it. Men needed women's votes so that "our American democracy might work as it was intended!"

"Oh, you good Hattie May," exclaimed Emily, under cover of the cheers of the audience.

> *Nov 4, 1911: Went to Freeville to visit George Junior Republic. Col. Roosevelt spoke, is not a good speaker, rather labored, not fluent. Refreshments were served in Howland Hall. I met Roosevelt. He is not awe-inspiring nor pleasing.*

As he was speaking, she had remembered how the Sherwood ERA had distrusted him when he was president. Several had feared that his enthusiastic military preparations meant he wished to plunge into a war.

On the other hand, knowing how slashing off their forests had desolated much of China and Africa, Emily favored his policy of protecting America's dwindling forests and natural resources for the next generation.

But still, eyeing him as he talked on in his over-loud voice, she had not been able to admire him.

Emily and Isabel marched with the Cayuga County contingent in the big 1912 suffrage parade in New York City. The next year saw an even larger New York parade. The few remaining old pioneers, including Emily, rode in "electrics," and all the women marching wore white. This was a massive show of strength, and Emily exulted to Isabel on their way home, "Even the colonel could not have criticized this parade for lack of decorum, could he?"

And Belle, agreeing, declared, "The tide of public conscience is turning in our favor, Aunt Emily. Surely the vote for women is not far off now."

When Harriet Tubman died in 1913 in Auburn, Emily promptly contributed to the fund for a memorial tablet honoring her old friend. Then she heard that Booker T. Washington was coming to Auburn to speak at the dedication. This was even more gratifying, for Dr. Washington's Tuskegee Institute, which she had visited several times, was a model for all the others. In addition to her frequent donations to his work, she had given an annual scholarship.

Thus, for this very special occasion, Isabel had taken front seats in a lower box in the Burtis Auditorium Theatre. She suspected that her aunt might be mentioned. At any rate, she must miss nothing.

Emily, therefore, with eyes wide and ears cocked, sat nearly on the stage. Looking about her, she saw the crowd filling the lower floor and all the boxes. Even the first families recognized that Harriet Tubman, though humble in herself, had been an important person.

The Festival Chorus led the audience in singing "The Battle Hymn of the Republic." Emily faltered at the words: "As He died to make men holy, let us die to make men free." She remembered Cornelia's harsh words on the lives that war had cost. And in the end, had it made men truly free?

Former Mayor Aiken presented the tablet which was later to be mounted on the Court House, saying: "Few memorials have been erected to women, and few to Negroes. None has been erected to one who was at once a woman, a Negro and a former slave. Harriet Tubman had the courage of a man!"

Emily heard no more of his high tribute. The courage of a man, indeed! Harriet Tubman had the courage of a lion! Or perhaps she had a reckless courage possible only to a woman who was also a Negro and a fugitive slave with a huge price on her head. She had nothing to lose, and as she had so truly said, "There's two things I got a right to, and these are Death and Liberty. One or the other I mean to have."

Now a neighbor rose to tell how Harriet had given refuge to indigent Negroes in her South Street home. Always there had been at least six or eight helpless and friendless wrecks in residence.

"On my going over to her house one morning, Harriet said cheerily that the meal chest was empty, so she prayed last night for a blessing, and 'when it come it was a poor blind woman, bad off with consumption an' her six chillern, one of 'em just a baby.' 'And what did you do?' I asked, dismayed at such a blessing. 'Oh, I did just what the Lord meant me to do,' Harriet answered, 'I scrummaged around 'mong the good people on South Street and got 'em something to eat and some clothes for them chillern. I tell the Lord what I needs an' He provides.'"

It was good to laugh, and it was good to see people wiping away a tear for this simplicity and goodness.

Suddenly, Rev. Lyman Ward's words flashed into Emily's mind: "Single-minded people are apt to be the world's saints." Harriet certainly wasn't saintly in the same way as the gentle old-time Quakers. And yet she did nothing but good for helpless people, mostly at her own expense, and often at the risk of her own life.

Emily looked around the crowded auditorium, and remembered assuring the Reverend Ward that Harriet was no saint. Now she asked herself, "I wonder if I wasn't wrong?"

And now the audience hushed as Dr. Booker T. Washington came forward and began to speak:

> "I am proud of my race tonight. I would not change my color or race with the whitest man in the country."

He went on in his dignified and sincere way, to laud Harriet as a great and unique character of whom any race should be proud.

> "No section of our country is richer in great heroic souls who believed in liberty for all people. Here lived the great Secretary of State who stood by Abraham Lincoln, William H. Seward.

> "In this section lived Susan B. Anthony. As I speak, I cannot forget Miss Emily Howland who, through her generosity and interest in all that concerns my race, has endeared herself to this and future generations."

And here he extended his hand toward Emily, and all in that auditorium turned to her and applauded.

When she could attend to his words again, he was telling of the progress of his race, their sacrifices to gain education, and the changes coming in the South.

And last he dedicated the tablet, inscribed:

> In Memory of Harriet Tubman
>
> Born a slave in Maryland about 1821;
> Died in Auburn NY March 10th 1913.
> Called the "Moses" of her people;
> during the Civil War, with rare courage
> she led over three hundred negroes
> up from slavery to freedom, and rendered
> invaluable services as nurse and spy.
>
> With implicit trust in GOD
> she braved every danger
> and overcame every obstacle, withal
> she possessed extraordinary foresight
> and truthfully said—
>
> "On my underground railroad
> I nebber run my train off de track
> and I nebber los' a passenger."

One October day in 1915, Harriet May, presenting herself at Emily's door with Isabel, handed her a card:

Miss Harriet May Mills
Ex-President New York State Woman Suffrage Association and
Chairman 5th District of Empire State Campaign for Woman
Suffrage will speak on the
WOMAN SUFFRAGE AMENDMENT
to come before the voter
November 2, 1915
in front of Dunn & McCarthy's Shoe Shop
from 12:25 to 12:45
This meeting is especially for voters
but women are also welcome.

Casting off her coat, Harriet May said, "We want you to lend your presence. Perhaps they might think we are flighty, but everyone respects you."

Emily, studying the card, objected, "Isn't it of first importance to convince the *women* that they need to be able to vote?"

Harriet May pointed out, "Only the men can vote to give them the vote."

"We've got to reach both," said Belle, "and that's why we're having this series of lunch hour rallies at factories. You will come to them, won't you?"

"And look your most dignified and proper," requested Harriet May. "Wear that hat of yours that looks like Queen Victoria."

Despite this series of meetings, and all the other efforts made statewide, the New York suffrage bill again failed. Emily looked sadly back over sixty-seven fruitless years of work.

Isabel, however, said, "We come closer each year, Aunt Emily. We'll campaign even harder next year. I feel it's just around the corner!"

Looming larger than this failure right now was the war news from Europe. All too well did Emily remember Cornelia's words about the waste of fine young men in the Civil War. To Belle she said, "It looks inevitable to me that America is going to be in this war soon."

Feb 5, 1917: President Wilson broke with Germany.

Mar 19, 1917: Czar of Russia has abdicated. What a topsy turvy world this is.

Mar 2, 1917: I am not idle. I read more since walking is painful. I must be glad for what I have and accept the lameness now as a part of my life.

Apr 5, 1917: War declared against Germany.

Apr 11, 1917: Went to Auburn. The streets were well beflagged. Every house had a flag out, plenty of stupid and speckled patriotism or exultation over the war that is on us.

May 17, 1917: The Dr. asked me how to live so long. I replied, "Think of yourself as little as you can and keep busy about something you think worthwhile."

June 1, 1917: Letter from Mr. Zabriskie entreating us to subscribe for the liberty loan. I have to borrow a large sum, so I could not venture on more than $50.

It is absurd to lend at 3 1/2% and borrow at 6%.

June 12, 1917: Isabel got a new car.

June 14, 1917: WCTU here. 13 in number, to make comfort bags.

Ever since Cornelia had revisited Little Deer in 1914, she and Isabel had been enthusiastically writing back and forth. This year their project was springing into being, and Isabel came bringing Emily the rough draft of a circular:

RESTAWHILE COTTAGE
Eggemoggin, Me.

Rooms in an old-fashioned farm house are available for self-supporting women desiring a restful and inexpensive vacation.

Fuel is supplied and the use of the kitchen is included in the charge of two dollars a week.

There are beautiful wood paths and boating and fishing on the Penobscot Bay afford healthful pursuits.

Eggemoggin is the steamboat landing where is located the post-office about a mile distant from Restawhile. A good grocery store is in the near neighborhood where during the season table supplies can be purchased.

As Emily lowered the sheet, Belle demanded, with eyes asparkle, "What do you think of that?"

"I like it, Isabel. People are always so much more interesting to me than mere scenery. I'll like to think of hard-working teachers and social workers enjoying a respite there, filling their lungs with that strong sea air."

Isabel and Harriet May had wound up their strenuous campaign in Syracuse, so Emily had to address the good news "in care of" the Mills home:

November 8, 1917

Dear Isabel,

Congratulations by phone and calls that Suffrage is won in New York State. I feel as though I was receiving as proxy for the absent and gone before. It seems too wonderful to be true.

I went to Auburn yesterday to get in touch with the spirit of the time. Mr. Bowen rolled us in thy car. We were requested to be at Headquarters by 10 a.m. to be photographed.

Everybody wished that thee was there.

It did seem too bad that thee could not be there at the last.

Aunt Emily

The elated women at headquarters had called on Emily for a few words. Rising heavily, she leaned her hands on the table. "So many years...so much struggle...so many thousands of petitions collected by Aunt Susan's women. And now that it has come in this State, all the old pioneers are gone." Then she went on more strongly, "Sixty or more years ago, Elizabeth Cady Stanton said men of color and all women were born to shame before the law. Gaining the ballot does not guarantee us equal rights, of course. But it is a giant first step." She looked around at her sobered listeners, too moved to say another word, and then sat down abruptly.

In 1918, Emily addressed the Sherwood graduates: "While the great war is upon us and its burden must be borne...hatred must be kept in abeyance. The interests of the world are so intertwined that everything done unhumanely injures all alike. The world is our country and all mankind our countrymen."

1920 was a joyful year for Emily, for not only had the great war been mercifully brief, but now the Prohibition Amendment made illegal the manufacture or sale of intoxicating beverages. Those abused women who had braved the wrath of their drunken brutes and tramped over muddy roads to sign her petitions were finally freed of the Devil Rum.

A neighbor who chanced to be present when Emily heard the news of the final ratification of nationwide Woman Suffrage that same year, later told Isabel, "Such a smile as came over her face!"

"I can hardly take it in," Emily had exclaimed, "I have seen the abolition of slavery, we have outlawed the liquor trade this year, and at last...at *last*, every American woman has the vote! Is my work finally done?"

Laurel: "Glory"

1921

Of course her work was not done! Emily had been working most of her life for the rights of her black friends and those of women and, yes, for her own. At the age of ninety-three, she certainly could not stop, even if she could only send checks to the many schools in which she was interested.

Now at last, she reluctantly sold the house on her plantation of dreams, Arcadia. There she had made independence possible for her colored friends. And there she had walked with the colonel. There they had eaten oysters and toasted their toes by her fire; there they dreamed briefly of the impossible being possible.

When Isabel had remarked, "Isn't it good to think of Cornelia up there on Little Deer Isle, harrying those pale professional women into deep breathing and long walks?" Emily had laughed comfortably, but she no longer traveled afar.

Now her interest centered in the "doings" of the little village of Sherwood and her school there. With the aid of Kit Cahalan, her sensible and kind housekeeper, she boarded the four high school teachers. It kept her young, she thought, to have them sitting around her big table each evening, correcting papers and planning lessons under the center light, while she, reading the newspaper, shared an occasional item.

All of them saved up tales of the youngsters' pranks to amuse her, and through them she came to feel she knew and understood her students rather well, despite the distance created by the young people's deep respect for her great age.

She recognized, however, that she lacked Isabel's knack of getting close to her neighbors and enjoying them wholeheartedly.

One day, Belle came bringing her a few choice blossoms in a fine glass vase. Emily admired them and sniffed of them, but then looked up sharply. "I hope thee does not use thy good vases for everybody!"

"Now, Aunt Emily," chided Belle, smilingly, "you wouldn't want me to take my pretty flowers to my friends in a jelly glass." She drew a chair closer.

"What has thee got on thyself?" Her aunt peered at her arm. "Some kind of red smears, they look like."

"Oh, I forgot about the mulberry juice." Isabel, with her soft laugh, rubbed her arm. "I was playing Indians with the boys. They were all painted up, you see, and when they tied me to the tree, I got a little of their 'war paint' on me."

Emily stared. "They tied thee to a tree? Why, I never heard the like of it! Why would thee let them do such a thing?"

Isabel laughed merrily. "I enjoy playing with the youngsters around the four corners. All I had to do was squeak a little and sigh 'Oh my, oh dear, what shall I do?' and we were all pleased."

As Emily shook her head in wonder, Belle teased, "You're a teacher to the bone. I suppose when you had Kit Cahalan's son and his friend to lunch, you talked improvingly to them."

Chuckling, Emily admitted, "I did, but they were so polite and long-suffering about it, I gave it up and showed them how to make a willow whistle."

Isabel, knowing Emily missed getting out more, liked to arrange little treats for her, and one day she came bringing a dish of oysters. Oh, how that took Emily back. Her thoughts flew to Virginia, where she had known such freedom and happiness. She remembered her special friends, Ella and Uncle Moses, and hoped their children and grandchildren were all prospering.

On the whole, though, she preferred to face forward.

> *Aug 1, 1923: Isabel and I have just had a visit from a Miss Grayson travelling in the interest of the National Woman's Party, organizing women and collecting funds to conduct campaigns for correcting laws discriminating against women.*
>
> *Alice Paul the leader. The militant doings that she introduced to haunt the White House seemed to me so absurd and unnecessary that I have little faith in her being a wise leader in any capacity.*

Despite her deep interest in her school next door, in 1926 she turned it over to the state as a public school to guarantee its survival after she was gone.

She complained laughingly when she was elected to the first board of education of the new consolidated public school. "Such nonsense, giving me, a ninety-eight-year-old, a five-year term! Do they imagine I am a female Methuselah?"

This reminded her that even she could not live forever and that what Father had left her had more than tripled in forty-five years. She positively must decide where all this property would do the most good.

Her bequests, after remembering her nieces and nephews, and dear friends and neighbors, included $1,000 apiece to most of the thirty-three schools she liked to fund. To Tuskegee, which had always been dear to her heart, even though her friend Booker T. Washington was gone now, she allotted $2,000.

As she considered Piney Woods, she thought of the Little Professor's letter saying, "I thought you would like to know that one staff member stood up all unbidden, during a Thanksgiving service in chapel, to call for a prayer for 'that good woman who gave us our printing press!'"

This had pleased her, for though it had been a small gift compared to their great need in those early days, it showed she had made a difference to them.

She never had been a major supporter of any of these industrial schools; each one had needed to find its own large supporters and endowments. But her smaller gifts scattered among them for specific needs had encouraged each of them to press on.

Well, and then there was Manassas, where she and the colonel had joined in their contributing.

After tapping her fingers for some moments, she firmly wrote $3,000 for both Piney Woods and Manassas.

> *June 19, 1926: This p.m. I did what I can never do again. I signed the diplomas of the graduates, 8 there were. They are the last that will be given by the dear old Sherwood Select School. There is a measure of sorrow in doing anything for the last time.*

As she set herself to writing her commencement address to her last graduates, she remarked, "What can I say that will be useful to these young people?"

Isabel smiled. "You don't need any help. You always find something memorable to say."

Emily shot a quick look at her. "The less you say, the more they remember."

When Emily received an invitation in 1926 to go to Albany to receive the first honorary doctorate in literature ever awarded a woman in New York State, she wrote to the commissioner of Education:

Dear Mr. Graves,

Your letter quite thrilled me by its urgent welcome to your Convocation with the added lure of receiving some honor of which I have but a vague idea. It surely would be a new sensation to be placed on a pedestal, but lack of strength forbids me to accept.

I shall cherish gratefully the memory of the kind thought.

Dr. Graves pressed her to accept the honor, saying it would help advance the cause of women's education, and Isabel added her coaxing.

"Now, Belle, do you realize I am almost ninety-nine years old? It is time for me to stay quietly by my fireside."

"Oh come, Aunt Emily, it isn't that at all. You know you've always loved to go places. It's just this terrible modesty of yours."

So, on October 29th, Emily did find herself on the platform in Albany before fifteen hundred persons, being lionized, as she called it.

Dr. Graves declared that, because she had been patron, teacher or member of the board of no less than thirty schools, "No one can number those who have been lifted to higher levels through the education opportunities that you have opened to them." And, to thunderous applause, he draped over her shoulders the purple and gold hood of a doctor of letters.

Back in her hotel room, while her friends gathered about her, chattering excitedly about the ceremony, she was presented with a basket of everlasting flowers. She chuckled, "Very suitable!"

Home again in Sherwood, she relived that day of glory in her mind. As she remembered the principal at Manassas coming to greet her, she realized, "Why, I never could have broken away from home except for the great need of the colored race." Whatever she had done for them, they had done more for her. And she wrote:

It was fitting that the race which opened the book of life for me should have been represented by the cultured Leslie P. Hill from Manassas.

Oct 27, 1926: Photographers came and despite my earnest dislike and protest, took a picture for the Syracuse

Post Standard which is the worst ever taken of me.

Nov 1, 1926: Many letters, one addressed to Dr. Emily Howland.

She stared at the envelope. "What an ironic twist to my early goal to be a doctor!"

Nov 24, 1926: My friends idealize me to such a degree that I am humiliated by knowing that their estimate is far above the true one.

Dec 1, 1926: Every mail brings letters of congratulations and over much laudation.

Commissioner Frank Graves was quoted as saying, "In nearly 150 years of the Board of Regents, Miss Howland is the only woman ever awarded an honorary doctorate, placing her in the class with university presidents, Supreme Court justices, ambassadors and our greatest scholars."

Even her nephew Herbert wrote ingratiatingly from Paris. Now that she was not embarrassing him with her dowdy presence among his society friends, he was most cordial and congratulatory. He signed himself, "Your loving nephew."

Dec 20 1926: I receive cards at every mail, many because I seem to have become a person of importance on account of the degree conferred. I cannot so regard myself.

Even after the holidays, notes of praise and congratulation dribbled in. Expecting another in the same vein, Emily slit open a letter which Belle had fetched from the mailbox.

Then she exclaimed, "Cornelia Hancock has died!" As Isabel turned to her in dismay, she continued fretfully, "Now why should her niece be telling me that Cornelia's effects are to be divided amongst her relatives?" Then her tone changed and quickened with interest, "except for a bundle of letters to be burned without reading."

"So!" Emily thought, "She *did* care for him, or she would have burned them herself, years ago."

From Isabel's startled expression, Emily realized how puzzling must appear her own nod of satisfaction, at the solving of a very old puzzle. Then full realization of their loss swept over her like a wave. Looking sadly at Belle, down whose face a tear was slowly running, she added in a deep voice, "She was the very last one of the grand old doers!"

Public school it might now be, but no commencement at Sherwood would have been complete without Miss Emily's address. Thus, in

June of 1927, she rolled slowly and majestically to school in her fringed horse-drawn carriage, remembering wryly how she'd walked several miles on her circuit of schools in Virginia, and now had to be driven even a few rods. But she forgot all that in looking about at the sea of faces of the students and most of her neighbors, respectfully watching her stately progress to the front of the hall on her driver's arm. She still had an important message to give them, written during Lindbergh's flight across the Atlantic. As she told the graduates and the hushed audience, straining to catch her every word:

> *I thought this is a prophecy, a symbol of the call to the*
> *young men and women of today to make all the world*
> *good neighbors.*

In September 1927, two months before her one hundreth birthday, the name of her school at Sherwood was officially changed to Emily Howland School. There was no honor which could have pleased her more than having this building bear her name in her home community. However, when one of the teachers who had formerly lived with her wrote in appreciation for all she had done, she answered:

Emily Howland shown after receiving her
honorary degree, October 29, 1926.

*When I thought I was doing for the public weal of my
community I was probably doing more for myself. For if
my experience & friendship gained by my relations with
that school were not a part of my life, a valued chapter
would be a loss I cannot measure, it goes into the realm
that has no limit.*

Emily had declared she dreaded her one hundredth birthday. As
she had expected, on that November Sunday, many of her friends
came to the informal open house that Isabel had arranged. She received, sitting in a rocker in the north parlor which was opened only
for funerals and special events. This room, with its tall mirror and
statuary and bric-a-brac, felt almost as unfamiliar to her as the appreciation and praise heaped upon her.

Amid the stream of smiling friends came Harriet May Mills.
Glancing at the line behind her, she remarked, "There are a lot of
grateful people here."

Emily chuckled. "I'm rewarded now for being out of step most of
my life. I never did fit in woman's proper sphere. Isn't it curious?"
and she handed Hattie a booklet.

"What's this?" and she read, *"What Price Peace* by Frederick
Libbey of the National Peace Council."

Emily countered, "Thee would not expect me to let all these people
come and go again, without my giving them an idea?"

Hattie grinned delightedly. "You never change! I see I must move
on, but Belle is letting me stay over, so we'll have another meeting
of the Great Triumvirate tomorrow."

Behind Harriet May, the keen-eyed Reverend Lyman Ward now
appeared. "I've seen you at several great occasions, the state convention in Auburn when you welcomed the National Suffrage dignitaries. And in Albany last year when you received your honorary
degree, I felt honored to represent the industrial schools of the South.
But this day crowns them all!"

His speech was so obviously memorized and rehearsed that she
took delight in answering, with a twinkle, "Indeed, yes. And as Susan Anthony ordered you, you've never asked me for a penny for
your institute."

He laughed heartily, now. "Fortunately, that has never stopped
you from donating to us."

Later, amidst the long line of faces, she greeted "young" William
Seward. "How glad I am to be reminded of your dear grandmother.
What a good friend she was to me."

He responded pleasantly, "Most people mention my grandfather to me. Very few knew Grandmother. I was born during the Civil War and she died that next year, so I never knew her."

"I count myself very fortunate indeed to have known her well from...why, from the time your father was in the nursery."

And then here was Katy...*Dr.* Munhall. Stooping to take one old hand in a firm clasp, she asked softly, "Do you want me to come now, Miss Emily?"

Emily hesitated and then admitted, "I would be glad if thee could. I feel lost since Dr. Hoxsie died this spring."

"Then I'll make my arrangements in Buffalo. It won't be long." Katy pressed her hand before she moved on. Emily looked after her with both love and relief.

At last the long line of callers ended. Now Emily could visit with small groups as they gathered about her rocking chair. Someone remarked, "I guess you must think these flappers are pretty bad, compared to your day."

"Why, no," she answered, surprised. "Girls are better, I think. In my time, they were neither to be seen nor heard. They are more natural now, and they have a better chance to become something." And then she added thoughtfully, "Yes, and young men are greatly improved, too. When I was a girl, they thought it was the thing to be fast and impertinent. Now they are ambitious."

To a comment that it was unusual for a woman of her age to be so active and interested, she said, decidedly, "Well, it shouldn't be! Every woman over seventy has something she always wanted to do and this is her opportunity."

Someone else asked Emily, "Have you always been so serene?"

"Serene?" she exclaimed. "I have never been serene! I have fought all my life for abolition of slavery, for education, for woman's suffrage, and for temperance. I have seen those victories come. Now it is up to you younger ones to work for world peace."

Isabel was the last to leave, and Emily asked, "Would thee please give me thine arm over to the other room before thee goes?"

Isabel settled her into her usual chair and then asked, "Do you realize that over a hundred people came today? And more wanted to but thought it would be too much for you. And look at this stack of telegrams and letters and cards!" She continued, "Leslie Hill has written from Manassas of all you've contributed there, the artesian well and the dormitory you built." Taking the letter out of her pocket, she read:

When I first went to Manassas as principal, Howland
Hall had already housed hundreds of girls who are now
serving their race as teachers. No one could compute the
good she has done in this world.

"And there's a lovely editorial in this month's *Tuskegee Messenger*. The writer starts by saying you helped in the making of Tuskegee Institute." Isabel looked in the pile of mail. "Yes, your copy has come, too." She opened up the paper and read:

Here is Emily Howland, a hundred years old this
month, a venerable soul whose life continues to be lived
out in unbiased, unprejudiced service.

Such a life as hers is like a candle in the darkness—a
warm, gleaming candle, burning steadily, steadily,
steadily, a little light by which to find the way to a real
living.

Emily had listened with her eyes down. Now she could not say a word, her heart was so full.

"Isn't that a beautiful tribute, dear? And all the more so because it is true." Isabel took her hand. "So many people love thee." Still holding her hand, she added, "Dear Aunt Emily, what a beautiful day!" After looking tenderly in her face for a moment, she turned to go.

Emily's eyes followed her to the door. Of all those dear people, this was the dearest, the best of them all. Her life, especially these late years, would have been a desert indeed without Belle.

Isabel looked back and they exchanged a last loving smile, before the door shut.

Emily leaned her head back now and took a deep breath. After resting a few minutes, she reached for her diary:

Nov 20, 1927: The day I have dreaded has come and
gone and I confess that I have enjoyed it. I can't see why
such a fuss is made over me. It is a misfit. I cannot apply
it to myself.

When she put her diary back in the drawer of the table at her elbow, she moved the papers around with her gnarled old fingers until she uncovered two treasures. Pulling them out, she laid them side by side on the table top and looked long at them. Then leaning her head back, she closed her eyes and looked back down over the years.

She roused at the opening of the door, as her devoted housekeeper and friend, Kit, peeped around at her. "Oh dear, are you tuckered to death after all that, Miss Emily?"

"No, I was just sitting here thinking." As Kit came over to her chair, she pointed first to the picture of the colonel and then to the certificate of her doctorate. "There were two ways I could have gone with my life. I could not have both."

Kit looked at the picture searchingly, for she had not seen it before. It was a fine strong face.

"But if I had chosen that way," explained Emily, touching his picture with a gentle finger, "I could not have done all that this represents." She took up the certificate and, looking at it for a moment, murmured, "I could not have shed even the little light that I have." Then putting it down, she drew a deep sigh.

Kit said anxiously, "You are tired out. Come and rest, Miss Emily," and leaned down to help her up.

Emily paused to put the picture and the certificate back in the drawer and slide it shut. Then taking Kit's arm, she walked to the window and looked out at the bell tower of the Emily Howland School.

"I hope someday it may be possible for a girl to have both," she mused as she went out on Kit's arm and the door closed behind her.

About the Author

Mildred D. Myers came, in a slower and simpler era, from a happy farm childhood, close family and community, in Chautauqua County, New York, to Syracuse University and thence to teach in a tiny Finger Lakes village filled with Howland history.

This proved to be a perfect situation for someone born in the wrong century, liking books so much more than TV or videos, a pen or typewriter so much more than computer, and *National Geographic* so much more than *Newsweek*.

Thus, during her ten years of teaching and many more as office manager in her husband's business, she greatly enjoyed getting into Emily Howland's life and times. And during the last twenty years, she also has been seriously researching and writing and rewriting Emily's story.

She and her tolerant husband, Ken, live in Scipio, and have three children who live nearby, who are more like friends than offspring and who have furnished them with four funny, creative and companionable granddaughters.